BY THE LONDON POST

Essays on Medicine
in Britain and America

JOHN
LISTER, M.D.

The *New England Journal of Medicine*
1440 Main Street, Waltham, MA 02254, USA

Library of Congress Cataloging in Publication Data

Lister, John

By The London Post

   Reprints of articles from the author's monthly column
in the *New England Journal of Medicine* from 1953–1984.
   Includes bibliographies and index.
   1. Medicine—Great Britain—Addresses, essays, lectures. 2. National Health Service (Great Britain)—Addresses,
essays, lectures. 3. Medicine—United States—Addresses,
essays, lectures. I. New England Journal of Medicine. II. Title. [DNLM: 1. National Health Service. 2. Medicine—
Great Britain—collected works. 3. State Medicine—Great
Britain—collected works. W 275 FA1 L75b]

R486.L57   1985   362.1'0941   85–10514
ISBN 0-910133-13-1

This book was set in 11 pt. Mergenthaler Baskerville #2
and composed at the facilities of the *New England Journal of
Medicine*. It was printed (on Sebago Antique 55#) and
bound by Murray Printing Co., Westford, MA, U.S.A.

Designed by Anne Chalmers
Cover illustration by Isabel Dempsey

To my wife Eileen
with thanks for her patience
and support for so many years

Contents

PART TWO
The National Health Service

 *Preface*

Joseph Garland, then editor of the *New England Journal of Medicine,* had a hunch that the urbane Englishman who dropped in to see him one April day in 1952 would be the perfect choice for a London correspondent. John Lister, a young consultant at the Royal Free Hospital in London, had already done some editing and writing, was interested in promoting closer contacts between physicians in the United States and the United Kingdom, and knew the world of British medical affairs intimately.

Lister's first "By the London Post" contribution appeared in the *Journal* of September 4, 1952. Garland wrote a short introduction in which he said: "One of the present stabilizing influences in the world is that the people of the British Commonwealth and those of the United States do speak and understand a common language and in many ways think along the same lines."

Garland could not have anticipated that he was launching what was to become a transatlantic institution. For the more than 28 years in which John Lister wrote his monthly piece for us, he fostered Anglo–American medical friendship more effectively than any physician of his time. He provided a generation of readers with a chronicle of medical and sociomedical events in his country, and he did it with common sense, good humor, and a felicity of style that gained him a legion of friends and admirers on both sides of the Atlantic.

The last regular "By the London Post" column, the 339th in

an unbroken monthly series, appeared in our issue of December 25, 1980. Since then, Dr. Lister has contributed occasional articles to the *Journal*, dealing with recent developments on the British medical scene and with the continued evolution of the National Health Service.

In the present volume we have collected a generous sampling of Lister's contributions, chosen in collaboration with the author to include what we believe are the best of his writings. They are arranged chronologically, in two parts. Part I deals with miscellaneous subjects, as they caught the discerning fancy of the author. Mostly they reflect the British medical scene, but some of the columns derive from Lister's numerous travels to America and elsewhere around the world. Part II is a collection of pieces about the National Health Service, selected to give a coherent and more or less continuous chronicle of important developments. In two recent pieces written for the *Journal* as "Occasional Notes," the story is brought up to date.

Assembled in this way, these columns offer more than simply the pleasure of reading an urbane and perceptive commentary on current medical affairs. They provide a knowledgeable first-hand account of the evolution of a unique national experiment in health care — one that is of interest to Americans as well as Britons. American and British people, as Garland said, tend to "think along the same lines." Sharing as we do so many cultural and historical roots, British and American physicians look at their profession in similar ways. We have our national characteristics, of course, but our professional values are much the same. That is why we Americans have been so fascinated by the British National Health Service and why we have learned so much from John Lister's dispatches.

But the greatest reward these pieces offer readers throughout the English-speaking world is the opportunity of getting to know a wise physician and keen observer of the human condition. In bringing the best of these articles together in book form this way, we make them conveniently available in one place. We hope this book will afford as much pleasure to new readers as to those who became addicted to the "London Post" during the three decades in which this series graced our pages.

Arnold S. Relman, M.D.
Editor, *New England Journal
of Medicine*

Introduction

When Dr. Joseph Garland invited me to write a monthly column for the *New England Journal of Medicine* in 1952, it never occurred to me that I would continue doing so for more than 28 years. The period 1952 to 1980 saw many changes in medical practice, and the British National Health Service (NHS) also underwent great changes over this period.

Dr. Garland chose the title for the column — "By the London Post." My brief was to interpret and comment on the British medical scene. This I tried to do as impartially as possible, although at times I know I was unable to conceal my own point of view.

Since 1948 British medicine has been thought of almost exclusively in terms of the National Health Service. This national institution was conceived by the liberal William Beveridge, introduced in 1948 by a Labour Government under the guidance of the charismatic Welshman Aneurin Bevan (who was Minister of Health), and since then has been accepted by successive governments as the British way of delivering health care to the majority of citizens in the country.

In the early years there was not too much controversy. Bevan had great difficulty in persuading the doctors to collaborate in running the NHS, but eventually he persuaded them to do so. He would have liked to establish a whole-time salaried service but this was quite unacceptable to the medical profession. The general practitioners, or family physicians, negotiated terms that allowed them to remain independent contractors, deriving their income mainly from capitation fees, and the hospital consultants and specialists were offered the option of whole-time or part-time contracts. Those accepting whole-time contracts were debarred from private practice, but those who opted for part-time contracts were allowed to combine private practice with their NHS hospital work. Furthermore, Bevan agreed to allocate a small number of hospital beds for the use of private patients.

These arrangements ensured that the doctors would collaborate in running the NHS, which they did with good will and enthusiasm for many years. However, in recent years the NHS has been subjected to serious political and financial pressures and has suffered greatly from the changing policies of successive governments. The administrative structure was reorganized in 1974 and again in 1982, and further administrative changes are now being planned.

In selecting topics for my monthly contributions I tried to cover as many aspects of the medical scene as possible. Inevitably, the various crises in the NHS were fully covered. At the same time I tried to include comments on ethical and educational matters of current interest, and because Dr. Garland had expressed the hope that the column would not be too dull, I even indulged in commenting on the occasional frivolous incident.

Much of what was written would not be of lasting interest. On the other hand, it seemed that by going through the various contributions it might be possible to select a collection of essays that would reflect the history and evolution of the NHS, with its vicissitudes over the years, as well as showing how the medical profession has adapted to the many changes to which it has been subjected.

Of course, having selected the topics for comment in the first instance and having selected the present collection as well, I realize that I am reflecting my own interests and prejudices. Indeed, in one respect the column has been of great therapeu-

tic value to me, for as Dr. Ingelfinger once suggested, it provided me with a unique opportunity not only for reflecting on
topics that interested me but also for working off my frustration
on many people whom I would never meet. For my own part I
can only say that my association with the *Journal* has been one
of the happiest experiences of my professional life and has led
to many lasting friendships.

I wish to record my thanks to the friends who have helped
me to select this collection of essays, and in particular I wish to
thank Mr. Leslie Morton, honorary librarian to the British
Postgraduate Medical Federation, for his advice and for com-
piling the index. I must also thank the editor, Dr. Arnold
Relman, and his staff at the *Journal* offices for their encouragement and forbearance.

JOHN LISTER, M.D.
Farm End, Burkes Road
Beaconsfield, Buckinghamshire
England HP9 1PB

 PART ONE

Thirteen Peripatetic "Posts"

 *The Royal Touch*

JULY 30, 1953

The reign of Queen Elizabeth II has already been a long one, and it seemed appropriate that the opening essay in this selection from the London Post should be one written in Coronation Year, in which the relationship between the Crown and medicine was considered.

Continuing the tradition of Royal patronage of medicine, Prince Charles honored the British Medical Association by accepting the office of President in 1982, when the Association was celebrating its 150th anniversary.

Coronation year has brought expressions of loyalty to the Crown from all sections of the community, and the medical profession has not been backward in paying its own homage. Many journals have published coronation issues, and these have recalled in special articles the longstanding royal patronage of the profession and the keen interest that many monarchs have taken in the health of their people.

E. Ashworth Underwood, in an article in the *British Medical Journal*, Coronation Number,[1] traces the relation between the Crown and medicine. He describes how St. Bartholomew's, the oldest London hospital and dating from 1123, came into being through the generosity of King Henry I. The Augustinian monk Rahere traveled from England to Rome, where he had a vision in which the apostle St. Bartholomew instructed him to "found at Smithfield a Tabernacle of the Lamp, a temple of the Holy Ghost." On his return to London he found that this site in Smithfield was owned by the King, who was, however, gracious enough to allow the monk to build a priory upon it with a hospital attached. Since the time of its early foundation, St. Bartholomew's has always cared for the "sick poor," and to the present day each new intern is reminded of this when he is given his "charge" concerning his duties.

After the dissolution of the monasteries Henry VIII took the revenue of St. Bartholomew's priory into his own hands and granted royal charters, under the terms of which the hospital is still chiefly administered.

It was also during the reign of Henry VIII that a certain organization of the medical profession took place. Surgery, medicine and the art of the apothecary had not previously been clearly differentiated, and quackery was rife. Thomas Linacre, physician to the King, was anxious for reform and was instrumental in framing an act of Parliament providing that no one should practice medicine within the City of London without passing an examination conducted by the Bishop of London or the Dean of St. Paul's. Six years later, in 1518, the King founded the College of Physicians, of which Linacre became the first president and to whose influence the foundation was largely due. The surgeons also became recognized during the same reign, and Thomas Vicary, who treated the king for varicose ulcers with temporary success, was largely responsible for the act of Parliament of 1540, which united the barbers and the surgeons in the Barber-Surgeons Company.

So it was that when Queen Elizabeth I ascended the throne in 1558, the physicians were just ceasing to be under the influence of the Church and the surgeons had been elevated to the dignity of a profession, but the apothecaries were still associated with the grocers. This last was the cause of much hard feeling. The physicians complained that the apothecaries not only compounded drugs but also saw patients, the apothecaries complained that the physicians not only saw patients but also compounded drugs and the grocers complained that the apothecaries sold not only drugs but also groceries. The apothecaries sought a remedy to the dispute by asking for a monopoly in the compounding and selling of drugs, but in spite of their representations, Queen Elizabeth I, in 1588, refused to grant them their request.

In any event, medicine progressed greatly in the days of Henry VIII and Elizabeth I, and through many successive reigns the medical profession has received the sovereign's encouragement and patronage. It is particularly appropriate to recall, at this coronation time, the practice known as the Royal Touch. As Dr. Underwood again states, the gift of healing by touching with hands was supposed to be conferred on the sovereign at his coronation. The practice dates in this country from 1066, when the king "cured an affected girl." The disease most commonly treated by touching was scrofula, or tuberculous cervical lymphadenitis, but patients suffering from other conditions were also brought for treatment. King Henry VII made the practice a religious ceremony and gave each patient a golden "angel," which was hung around the neck. Charles II is said to have touched 90,000 persons in nineteen years, and Pepys has described the religious ceremony as carried out in his day. Queen Anne used the practice as a means to demonstrate her hereditary right to the throne, and Samuel Johnson was among her patients when he was brought as a child of two and a half years, with tuberculous lymph nodes in the neck. The custom finally disappeared on the accession of George I, and since that time the sovereign's interest in the people's health has become based on the sound scientific advances of modern times. In this respect, it seems fitting that in the month before Queen Elizabeth II was crowned, she laid the memorial stone of the new Royal College of Surgeons in Lincoln's Inn Fields. Much of the college was destroyed by enemy action in 1941, and the new building is designed to enlarge the institution to accommodate all its scientific and educational activities. At the ceremonial laying of the stone, Sir Cecil Wakeley, president of the College, said that the great hall would be the heart of the new college, where its scientific and social meetings would be held. Above the hall there would be three new floors to accommodate laboratories and museums, and at a later stage a new residential block is to be built by the generosity of the Nuffield Trust, chiefly for overseas students. Perhaps the Queen's laying of the foundation stone of this great new project in her coronation year may be regarded as a contemporary Royal Touch, from which it may be hoped that many thousands far from Lincoln's Inn Fields will derive benefit.

---

1. Underwood EA. Medicine and crown. Br Med J 1953; 1:1185-1191.

The Medical Traveler

All those who have enjoyed international travel and the stimulus of meeting with colleagues will recognize the various syndromes described with such perception by Prof. L. J. Witts, the late Nuffield Professor of Clinical Medicine at Oxford.

The medical traveler is no new phenomenon. Long ago Paracelsus, who was born near Zürich, said that a doctor must be a traveler because he must inquire of the world. He himself set out on his travels in 1513. His tour lasted twelve years and first took him to Bologna and Padua in Italy. Thence he went to France, Spain, the Netherlands and Sweden and later journeyed east to Turkey and Russia. Thomas Linacre, who became the first president of the Royal College of Physicians in 1518, graduated at Oxford and then went to Italy to travel. John Caius of Cambridge, who was president of the College from 1555 to 1560, studied medicine at Padua, where he lodged in the same house as Vesalius. It was at Padua, too, that William Harvey studied medicine, graduating there with high honors in 1602.

All down the ages medical men have continued to visit centers of learning in foreign lands to study, to lecture and to meet their professional colleagues, and since the last war they have done so in ever-increasing numbers and at ever-increasing speed. Indeed, it is now possible to classify a number of differ-

7

ent types of medical travel and a number of different types of traveler, and this has been done with particular lucidity by Professor Witts in his reflections in the *Lancet* on a recent tour of the Far East. He considers first what he defines as the omnium-gatherums, or vast international congresses, to which large numbers of doctors gravitate each year. He recalls how enjoyable was the first international congress of internal medicine in Basle in 1946 and laments that many such meetings have subsequently tended to become too large, too organized and too expensive. Each congress now has a long period of gestation, and many papers are out of date by the time they are delivered. The regular performers of the stage army are rapidly aging, the level of presentation is often poor, the opportunity for discussion is usually lacking, and it becomes increasingly difficult to meet one's friends unless a rendezvous is previously arranged. Even though this may be too gloomy a picture of the international congress, there is perhaps a danger that congresses have become too large and too frequent if their object is the advancement of medicine and the promotion of friendship among physicians. On the other hand they still make a focal point for meeting, and even if the formal meetings are of limited value, the off-stage contacts between physicians are always of value.

Apart from the large number of doctors who gravitate each year to such omnium-gatherums there has also been a growing stream of individuals who journey to all parts of the earth as traveling fellows, visiting professors, examiners and medical experts. These are the true successors of the medical traveler of days gone by, and Professor Witts believes that such solitary migrants have an increasingly important part to play in the development of medicine.

He recognizes three types of academic foreign travel: the visit, the progress, and the sortie. The visit is perhaps ideal because it allows the traveler a period varying from some weeks to a full sabbatical year, during which he may settle down in a center where he may get to know the local staff, take part in teaching programs and even have temporary charge of beds. The progress type of trip is more suited to the young man's needs than those of the mature professor. It should last not more than three months, and during this time a number of centers may be briefly visited. It has many advantages in that a wide field of interest can be covered in a short time, but it is also liable to all the disadvantages of the conveyor-belt system. Thus, the traveler tends to be carried on a conveyor belt under the aegis of a sponsoring organization, and the belt moves inexorably along. Life is a succession of academic and social engagements and restless travel, with all the attendant strains on the cortical cells, the coronary arteries and the gastric mucosa. Thirdly, there is the sortie, whereby the traveler, instead of taking a long leave of absence, attempts to look after his practice or his department and at the same time makes brief dashes across the ocean to fulfill some visiting engagements. This is a pernicious form of expedition and indicates a misguided sense of personal indispensability.

After all these types of travel, there is likely to be a period of reactive depression, which afflicts many travelers on their return home and which Professor Witts has called the repatriation syndrome. It has several components, the most important being fatigue, the accumulation of tasks and problems during absence and the switching off of the limelight in which the traveler has basked so happily.

In the days of Paracelsus, Linacre, Caius and Harvey the progress type of trip and the sortie were out of the question because they were spared the opportunity of traveling by air, by train or by fast oceanliners. Even the sabbatical year would have seemed a hurried visit and given little margin for traveling time. No doubt they were thus spared the repatriation syndrome. Nevertheless, in spite of the urge to travel quickly and the unwieldy size of many modern international congresses, the opportunity of meeting with medical men from other countries, often with widely differing ideologies, must help to foster better understanding, not only between professional colleagues but also between the countries to which they belong. Thus, at the third congress of the International Union of the Medical Press recently held in London, it was a stimulating experience to meet editors representing medical journals from twenty-nine countries, and in particular to have the privilege of seeing the editor of the *New England Journal of Medicine* take a leading part in the proceedings. Even though at times during his trip he may have felt as though he were being carried on a conveyor belt, I am sure that a leisurely sea voyage home will prevent any likelihood of his contracting the repatriation syndrome and that it will not be too long before he pays us another visit, if necessary to attend another omnium-gatherum.

Thoughts on Anniversaries, Jubilees, and Centenaries

AUGUST 28, 1958

The first decade of the National Health Service was completed in the same year as the Royal Army Medical Service celebrated its diamond jubilee and 100 years after Charles Darwin and Alfred Russel Wallace presented to the Linnaean Society their paper on the origin of species and the descent of man.

Ten years after the NHS was introduced, its major benefits and major problems had already been identified. Many more anniversaries have been celebrated since 1958, but although the benefits of the Service continue to be enjoyed by the general public, many of the problems remain unresolved.

It seems that nearly all ancient people celebrated the return of spring and the death of winter each year, and it was from this custom that anniversaries, jubilees and centenaries have come to be celebrated in commemoration of events of personal, national and political importance. There is always the danger in such commemorations of looking back in complacency rather than looking forward in inspiration, and if the occasion is to be put to good use it is clear that the emphasis must be on the latter.

This year, the National Health Service celebrates the tenth anniversary of its inception, and the occasion has been marked by Parliamentary debate and by the publication of special supplements both in the lay and in the medical press. In particular, *The Times* and the *British Medical Journal* have published supplements in which the achievements of the first decade of the National Health Service have been critically reviewed. There is general agreement that from the point of view of the patient the Service has conferred enormous benefits. There is no longer any need for a financial barrier between doctor and patient because all the professional care that may be needed for the treatment of all kinds of accident or illness is available without charge. The aspects of the Service that give cause for anxiety are its continually mounting cost, and especially the ever rising national drug bill, the doctor and his pay, the lack of new hospital building and a tendency for the medical profession to become disintegrated within itself. This tendency is partly due to the fact that the hospital services, the general-practitioner service and the public-health services are all differently administered. Indeed, it has been suggested that the future holds a challenge for an inspired administration, and it certainly seems that many of the problems could be eased by administrative reforms. At the same time it is clear that the challenge to the profession is to preserve its own integrity and to work for the better integration of the various aspects of medicine such as teaching, research, preventive medicine, occupational health and the hospital and general-practitioner services. But it must be acknowledged that much has been accomplished in ten years and traditions take far longer to build up than this.

Another special anniversary this year has been the Diamond Jubilee of the Royal Army Medical Corps. During its sixty years of service great traditions have been built up, but long before Queen Victoria signed the Royal Warrant that brought the Corps into being, there was a well established tradition of medical military service. During the Napoleonic wars, George Guthrie (1785–1856) became famous and earned the name of the "British Larrey" because his reputation so nearly rivalled that of Dominique Jean Larrey, who served Napoleon so outstandingly as chief surgeon. Guthrie started his career as a surgeon apprentice, and when only sixteen he entered the Army as a "hospital mate" at the York Hospital, Chelsea. He then served in Canada and later had as many as 3000 wounded men under his care during the Napoleonic wars. He also stressed the need for the teaching of military surgery, and he and others urged that the medical services of the Army should be better organized. Nevertheless, when the Crimean War broke out in 1854 there was no organized medical corps, and each regiment had to rely on recruiting its own medical officer. The disastrous experience of that war no doubt gave impetus to the formation of the Royal Army Medical Corps in 1898. From that time, all the medical services of the Army were organized within one corps commanded by its own medical officers and having its own ranks and its own uniform, bearing the motto "In arduis fidelis."

Many great names have been associated with the Corps, and many contributions have been made to the advances in civilian medicine as the result of military experience. Thus, the combined efforts of Almroth Wright and Boog Leishman at the Army Medical College resulted in the development of preventive inoculation against typhoid; Leishman himself devised a simple method of staining the malarial parasite and made original observations on the cause of kala-azar, which is also known by his name. The achievements of the Corps during the two world wars are well known, both in the field of preventive medicine and in the realms of traumatic surgery. In particular the opportunities for carrying out trials with the early antibiotics and in developing blood-transfusion services were brilliantly seized, and the experience gained has been incorporated in civilian medical practice. Although the future of the Service must seem somewhat uncertain, it can look back over the years with just pride in its achievements and in the traditions that it has established.

Having looked back on ten years of the National Health

Service and sixty years of the Royal Army Medical Corps, one is also interested to recall that a hundred years have now passed since Charles Darwin and Alfred Russel Wallace presented to the Linnaean Society their paper on the origin of species and the descent of man. Since the presentation of this paper and the publication of his book on the origin of species in the following year, Darwin's theory of evolution has, of course, become generally accepted, and he has been regarded by many as the founder of scientific biology.

From an early classical education at Shrewsbury School Darwin went to Cambridge, where he was happy and sociable, with a passion for bird hunting. He then spent two years in Edinburgh studying medicine, but abandoned this course and had the intention of entering the Church, when, in 1831, he had the opportunity of setting sail on a five-year voyage in southern waters as naturalist to the expedition of *H.M.S Beagle*. This proved the turning point in his career, and his diary of the voyage reveals how he set out methodically to make the observations that enabled him to support his theory of evolution. The theory having been accepted, it should follow that, because evolution is a dynamic and not a static phenomenon, man's destiny will be the instrument of further evolution on earth. Making this point in a special article in the *Sunday Times* to commemorate the Darwin Centenary, Sir Julian Huxley warned that evolution could be retrogressive rather than progressive, a deviation instead of an advance. He pointed out that it is therefore up to mankind to discover and realize new and richer possibilities for life. This is certainly a privilege, but also a grave and almost frightening responsibility.

It is perhaps significant that Darwin's early education was classical, and although he thought little of its value at the time, it clearly contributed to his capacity for fundamental thought. Thus, although in his memoirs he recalled that "nothing could have been worse for the development of my mind than Dr. Butler's school, as it was strictly classical, nothing else being taught except a little ancient geography and history," he did concede that while at school he developed a taste for long, solitary country walks, which gave him a chance to think and study nature. Surely, here must be found some clue to his later success, and surely, in looking ahead rather than looking back over the years, the great need today is for men of the caliber of Darwin to have time to take solitary walks and think.

United We Stand, Divided We Fall

MARCH 26, 1959

The role of the physician in society has undergone many changes, as described in this essay written in 1959. However, the greatest change in Britain took place when the state intervened in 1948 and assumed major responsibility for the delivery of health care. This altered the relationship between patients and doctors and introduced a new relationship between the doctor and the state. These changes created problems for the profession that are still not solved.

Thus, agreement with the government on matters concerning remuneration remains elusive. Many young physicians and surgeons are still having difficulty in finding permanent posts, and their problems have been aggravated by reduced opportunities for emigration, so that unemployment is genuinely feared. Finally, the profession still tends to be divided, the interests of hospital consultants being different from those of general practitioners (family physicians), and those of junior staff in the hospital being different from those of established consultants.

In a recently published book, *Call the Doctor: A social history of medical men* (London: Michael Joseph, 1958), Mr. E. S. Turner has drawn a portrait of the doctor through the ages as a member of society. The author admits that, being a layman, he has never dissected a leg, certified a lunatic or been called from his bed to sniff the breath of an abusive alderman. However, he has not attempted to write a history of medicine, but in his character study he has shown how the doctor, in spite of his high calling, has often been a controversial figure.

Beginning with the doctors of Chaucer's day, he describes how the code of behavior of the physician of that time was represented by the views of men like John of Gaddesden, who was depicted as the Doctor of Physic in the *Canterbury Tales* and was also the first Englishman to hold the appointment of court physician.

The physician was advised to dress soberly, like a clerk and not like a minstrel. He should behave modestly at all times and should tell the patient that with God's will he should recover, but the relatives should be informed of the gravity of the case. Recovery was then a testimony to the physician's skill, but if his patient died he had safeguarded himself. Doctors were urged not to disparage their colleagues and advised to avoid the company of laymen because they made a habit of mocking doctors, and besides it is not always easy to extract fees from intimates.

By the fifteenth century the vested interests of medicine were beginning to jostle each other. The main groups were the physicians, the apothecaries, the surgeons and the barbers, with such others as quacks, midwives, herbalists and alchemists all trying to press their claims.

It was in 1518 that the more learned members of the profession formed themselves into the Royal College of Physicians under the leadership of Thomas Linacre. Entrusted with the granting of licenses to practice, the College did much to spread the new medical and anatomic knowledge. The surgeons were only a small fraternity, their social status was poor and their manner rough, and their alliance with the barbers in 1540 was one of expedience. Much quarreling took place between the physicians and the Barber-Surgeons Company, especially over the prescription of drugs, which was only allowed to the physicians — ostensibly to protect their patients, but more probably to protect themselves.

After Harvey's discovery of the circulation of the blood in the early seventeenth century, medicine went through a period of great flux, and progress was influenced both by philosophy and by the new science. It was in the eighteenth century that the gold-headed cane became the physician's symbol of office and helped to impress the patient. This was important because there was considerable cynicism about the doctor's capabilities, and indeed Voltaire believed that the physician was a man who poured medicine of which he knew nothing into a body of which he knew less. Nevertheless, at that time the London physician was often rich and his social standing high, but in contrast the rural practitioner was humble and of modest means. Content to ride his horse over miles of bog and moor every year for perhaps £200, he had to be physically strong and mentally alert. Many of his patients were desperately poor, and it is said that Dr. Fothergill, a Quaker physician of that time, often made the act of feeling the pulse a cover for slipping money into the patient's hand.

Few episodes have ever created a deeper rift between the medical profession and the public than the spate of body snatching at the end of the eighteenth century. The activities of the so-called resurrectionists who seized newly buried bodies were perhaps condoned, but the hue and cry was uncontrolled when the notorious practices of the like of Burke and Hare were exposed as a national scandal. At about the same time the medical student came to be regarded as one of nature's wilder characters, and in the early part of the nineteenth century he was not infrequently considered an unrepentant grave robber, a swaggerer and a drunkard and not even beyond suspicion of practicing vivisection.

During the latter part of the nineteenth century the rise of the surgeon was given great impetus by the discovery of anesthesia and antiseptic principles, and the day began to dawn when an operation was a smart thing to have. At the same time the gold-headed cane disappeared; the patient chose the doctor who gave the best results at the right price, and the general practitioner began to assume the role of family counselor and friend. But once more, in Edwardian times, the doctor became anxious about his status. Specialization was increasing, medicine was advancing, and the busy practitioner was finding difficulty in keeping abreast. In 1906 *The Doctor's Dilemma* was first put on the stage, and in his preface to the play Bernard Shaw suggested that the doctor's self-respect would be increased and his temptations diminished if he were paid a fixed salary. The medical profession could then become "a body of men trained and paid by the country to keep the country in health."

Here, then, were the words that were to herald the call for socialization of medicine. First came Lloyd George's National Insurance Bill in 1911, providing against sickness for all workers earning less than £3 a week. The doctor would receive 6 shillings a year for each person on his books. The bill was resisted by the profession, but when free choice of doctor was ensured for the patient and certain assurances were given to the doctor the British Medical Association agreed to co-operate. These measures worked quite well, but dependents of workers were not insured in any way. The increasing cost of medical care, the financial embarrassment being felt by the majority of voluntary hospitals and the dream of a comprehensive welfare state were the main social factors leading to the National Health Service in 1948. In principle it was accepted by both political parties, but the doctors entered the service with mixed feelings. Some were glad to be relieved of the burden of buying a practice and were glad to accept the security of state payment. Others were sure that such acceptance could only lead to ever-increasing state control and eventually a whole-time salaried service as envisaged by Bernard Shaw. With this they saw a permanent loss of social status. Many young men hoped that greater opportunities than hitherto would be open to them in hospitals in the fields of specialization and research. Most of the established consultants accepted the Service as inevitable and hoped that any loss in private practice would be offset by the salaries they would be paid for their hospital work previously done voluntarily.

And so one looks at the doctor of today after ten years of the National Health Service. The general practitioner believes that his respect in the eyes of his patients has tended to fall because the facilities of investigation and treatment he can offer are so outmatched by those available at the hospitals. He is not encouraged to improve his own office premises because he receives no financial help for doing so. Indeed, the subject of payment is one of which most practitioners are heartily sick. Spens reports, Royal Commissions on remuneration, independent enquiries and announcements of 4 per cent interim increases are phrases that buzz in their ears like constant tinnitus. And yet the latest report by a retired civil servant claims that the average family doctor is reasonably content and not showing any real signs of frustration.

In the hospitals younger men who have succeeded in obtaining consultant appointments are doing well but are often bogged down by bureaucrats and their committees. But many young men highly trained in special fields are unable to obtain permanent posts. Many of these, and others too, have had to seek work overseas, and the recent wave of medical emigration cannot fail to be a matter of concern. And so once more, as so often in the past, the medical profession is in a state of flux, and the doctor himself is a controversial figure. Certainly, the National Health Service is partly responsible, but as in earlier days the doctor is partly to blame. Just as the physicians were pitted against the apothecaries and the surgeons against the barbers, so the interests of the general practitioner and the consultant are often at variance today.

Again, the structure of the National Health Service is partly the cause because the general-practitioner service and the hospital service are quite separately administered. Nevertheless, no matter how much strength the profession may have gathered in the past from the individualistic character of many of its illustrious members, there can be no doubt that its weakness today, in its negotiations with the Ministry of Health, chiefly lies in the fact that it is divided within itself.

Doubtless there is much to be written yet of the twentieth-century British physician, but when it is written, there is no doubt that the doctor will still appear as a controversial figure. Nevertheless, the present demand should be for unity within the profession itself because a divided profession can never be strong: united we stand — divided we fall.

The Lancet *and the Wakley Tradition*

JULY 26, 1962

The *Lancet* is the oldest medical journal in Britain and second only to the *New England Journal of Medicine* in the order of seniority of such journals throughout the world. Thomas Wakley, the founder and first editor, was a man of many parts.

———

In a recent issue of the *Lancet* Dr. W. H. McMenemey portrayed a remarkable character study of Thomas Wakley, the founder and first editor of that journal, who died a hundred years ago on May 16, 1862. Born in 1795 into the large family of a Devon farmer, he spent his early days in the open air and did not excel with his books but was known for his wit and love of sport. At the age of fifteen he was apprenticed to an apothecary, and seven years later he became a member of the Royal College of Surgeons and began to practice in the City of London. In his student days he had already witnessed some of the injustices of the day, such as the dependence of the anatomists and their students upon the resurrectionists and the criminal-court judges for a supply of corpses, the bidding for places in the entourage of the leading consultants, the blatant nepotism in the colleges and hospital boardrooms and the prosperity of quacks.

Being a man of liberal tendencies and of exceptional vigor of body and mind, he was clearly marked out for an outstanding and probably stormy career, and he early decided to set about reforming the profession by means of his pen. His subsequent achievements stem from his triple career as founder and editor of the *Lancet*, as member of Parliament for Finsbury and as coroner for West Middlesex.

The first issue of the *Lancet* appeared on October 5, 1823, and distinguished physicians and surgeons were soon alarmed to see their lectures in print and feared a falling off in student fees and attendance. Charlatans and proprietors of patent medicines realized that their secrets would be exposed, and the members of the Council of the Royal College of Surgeons found themselves attacked in the editorials. Wakley was soon branded as a literary pirate and public enemy of the privileged few who ruled within the profession, and became involved in a series of lawsuits. One of these occurred in 1828, when he dramatized an unfortunate incident of lithotomy at Guy's Hospital, following it with the autopsy report. The surgeon, Mr. Bransby Cooper, nephew of Sir Astley Cooper, sued him for libel, and although Cooper won the action, the court's tacit admiration for Wakley was reflected in the award of damages of only £100 instead of the £2,000 claimed.

In spite of his forceful pen Wakley believed that he would need to find a place in Parliament before he could achieve the reforms he considered necessary. He eventually obtained his election in 1835 and remained a member for seventeen years. During this time he saw the introduction of the Vaccination Bill (1840), the revised charter for the Royal College of Surgeons (1843) and his own Medical Witness Bill (1836). He attempted unsuccessfully to bring in a medical-registration bill to outlaw quackery, but this did lead to the setting up of the Select Committee on Medical Registration and served as a basis for the Medical Act of 1858.

In his capacity as coroner for West Middlesex, to which he was elected in 1839, he had further opportunity for uncovering injustices and publicizing them in the columns of the *Lancet*.

The strain of his three exacting appointments eventually

took its toll, and the last ten years of his life were marred by ill-health and the eventual development of a persistent cough with occasional hemoptysis. In spite of a spes phthisica he was aware of his fate, and in the autumn of 1861 he sailed to Madeira to escape the English winter. It was on the quayside there that he slipped during the following May, and died from a severe hemoptysis a few days later.

Wakley was clearly a man of great determination, and he was also a man of great character and courage who cherished the inspiration and discipline of a Christian upbringing and saw where his duty lay. The righting of wrongs was for him perhaps a vocation rather than an obsession. Of all the tributes paid to his memory to mark the centenary of his death the one that would probably have astonished him most was paid at the Royal College of Surgeons. Making the May monthly dinner a Wakley occasion, the President, Sir Arthur Porritt, described him as belligerent but a man of ideas, who in retrospect could be seen to have done nothing but good for the College. But of course, the greatest tribute of all is the continued vitality of the *Lancet*. This vitality, which was the outstanding character bequeathed it by the first editor, was maintained by the successive members of his family who filled the editorial chair for another forty-seven years. After Thomas Wakley died in 1862 his youngest son, James, succeeded him, and he, in turn, was followed by an elder brother. When this third editor died in 1907, his son, another Thomas Wakley and the grandson of the founder, became editor, but died in 1909. At this time Sir Squire Sprigge, who was Wakley's biographer, was appointed editor, being succeeded in 1937 by Egbert Morland, and it was in 1944 that Dr. T. F. Fox, the present editor, assumed his office.

In the many celebrations that have recently taken place to commemorate the first editor and founder, his great-grandson, yet another Thomas Wakley, and Dr. Fox both played a leading part. These celebrations included a service in the parish church in the village of Membury, Devon, where he was born, a ceremony of remembrance at Harefield Hall in Middlesex, where he had a country house for a short time, and the unveiling of a plaque by Dr. Fox at 35 Bedford Square, London, which Wakley occupied as his townhouse for many years.

Throughout the years the *Lancet* has always held a special place in British medicine. Its early attitude of belligerent crusading has mellowed with time, and its radical views have become more liberal until today the high standard of its scientific articles and the independent point of view of its editorials are its outstanding characteristics. It is therefore not surprising that the fear of publication of their lectures, which obsessed the medical-school teachers of former days, has been replaced by a hope by their counterparts of today that such lectures may appear in the columns of the *Lancet*. Similarly, the pressure from anxious young authors to have their original papers published puts an ever-increasing strain on the editor and his colleagues.

The continued respect in which the *Lancet* is so widely held is in no small way due to the influence of Dr. Fox, and it is particularly appropriate that he should have been honored only this spring by a knighthood conferred upon him by the Queen.

Twice each year, on New Year's Day and on the Queen's official birthday, a group of men and women in all walks of life who have distinguished themselves in their service to their country, whether in their professions or businesses or in the field of art or sport, are honored by the Sovereign. Many honors are open, some of special significance, such as the Royal Victorian Order, which was created by Queen Victoria for services rendered specifically to the Sovereign. Distinguished members of the medical profession are often prominent in these honors lists, and besides Dr. Fox the recent list includes the names of Dr. George Godber, chief medical officer at the Ministry of Health, Surgeon Vice-Admiral

W. R. S. Pankridge, medical director of the Navy, and Dr. H. C. Colville, the first president of the Australian Medical Association, all of whom are also knighted.

In congratulating Dr. Fox, the *British Medical Journal* has recalled his quizzical observation of the medical scene at home and abroad and how he has delighted his readers with accounts of his travels. His recent thoughts on the continued need for the personal physician have reflected the views of many who are acutely conscious of the changing pattern of medical practice and of the many conflicting loyalties confronting the doctor today. Dr. Fox's interest in social reform is well known, and this has perhaps helped him to maintain the Wakley tradition in a way that has won for him the admiration of all his colleagues in medical journalism, as well as the respect of a much wider sphere of friends.

So long as the affairs of the *Lancet* are in the hands of men like Sir Theodore Fox, there will be no doubt that it will be a journal worthy of being the oldest medical journal in Britain, and second only to the *New England Journal of Medicine* in the order of seniority of such journals throughout the world.

The Royal College of Physicians of London

DECEMBER 31, 1964

The hope expressed by Mr. (now Sir) Denys Lasdun that in time all those who used the newly opened College building would grow to like it has largely been fulfilled. Situated in St. Andrew's Place, Regent's Park, London, it has become a familiar landmark, and it is hoped that the acquisition of surrounding property will permit a medical precinct to be established in this area.

The history of the College has been published in three volumes by the Oxford University Press. The first and second volumes are written by Sir George Clark, and the third by Dr. A. M. Cooke of Oxford.

The Royal College of Physicians of London has now moved into its fifth home, which was formally opened by the Queen on November 5. In her speech the Queen recalled the close connection that the College has had with the Royal Family since King Henry VIII's physician successfully petitioned the King to found it in 1518. She thought it would not be surprising if Thomas Linacre had found his patient rather difficult and had the wise idea of sharing his responsibilities with other distinguished members of the profession. Sir Charles Dodds, the president, pointed out, however, that this was the first time in the history of the College that the Sovereign had been present in person at the opening of one of its new homes.

Sir Robert Platt, past-president, in thanking the Queen for

her gracious visit, spoke of the day in March, 1962, when the Queen Mother had laid the foundation stone of the new building. He had referred then to the somewhat erratic monarch Charles II, who had promised the College a new charter to establish its claim to the Royal title. This had never materialized, but the fellows had continued to use the title until this new move was contemplated, when the Parliamentary lawyers caught up with them and questioned their credentials; fortunately, a new act of Parliament had now been passed, and all was well. He then hastened to assure Her Majesty that even on November 5 she could be in no safer and more loyal place than the Royal College of Physicians of London.

The opening celebrations were continued on the following day at a special conference, when Sir George Clark, professor of history at Oxford, who has just completed the first volume of the history of the College, described the place of the College in English social history. He pointed out that it is the oldest English medical institution and that its foundation in 1518 by King Henry VIII was to satisfy a need and meet an emergency.

In Tudor times medicine was backward in England as compared with the Continent, and physicians were not bound together. Epidemics were rife and encouraged the appearance of unqualified practitioners; 1518 was a plague year, and it was then that Thomas Linacre and a few colleagues petitioned the King that they might be incorporated into a college. The Sovereign agreed to do so and granted a charter to set up a college with authority to grant licenses to practice, to punish pretenders and offenders and to have authority over apothecaries in London and for 7 miles around. After its foundation the College met regularly at Linacre's house south of St. Paul's Cathedral and continued to do so until 1614, when the house became inadequate for its purpose and a more suitable one was purchased at Amen Corner and became the second home of the College. Both Linacre's house and the Amen Corner College were destroyed in the Great Fire of 1666. On this occasion Dr. Christopher Merrett was able to remove about 140 books, the College records and Harvey's portrait to safety, although in the previous year he had been held responsible for the loss of numerous College treasures, which were stolen when he retired to the country, with most of the officers, to escape from the plague. After the fire the College moved to a new site in Warwick Lane, where it remained until the move to its fourth home in Pall Mall East in 1825.

Sir George explained that the early history of the College was shaped by the exceptional character of London, which dominated political and industrial life more than other capitals of Europe. Professional bodies at that time were very rare, and for nearly a hundred and fifty years it remained the only medical body in London and the only learned society outside the universities until the foundation of the Royal Society in 1660. In manners and customs it was academic, but there was no university in London when the College was founded and Linacre relied on the English and Continental universities for teaching, although John Caius, who succeeded him as president, brought a new impetus to the College and introduced anatomic demonstrations for London practitioners. It was in the lecture theater at the Amen Corner College that Harvey lectured and presented his museum. There, too, the College received its first visit from a reigning sovereign when Charles II presented a piece of unicorn's horn, which was lost in the Great Fire. Sir George said that the new building in Warwick Lane became one of the regular sites for visitors, and a French guidebook recommending a visit urged the tourist to offer at least 3 pence to the person who showed him around.

The moves from one site to another within the city of London did not signify any change in function of the College, and although its status may have varied and its authority in granting licenses declined with the appearance of new universities, it did give advice on medical subjects to successive governments.

Thus, its advice was sought on such varied problems as the control of epidemics and other public-health matters, the medical service to the Army, reports of cases of witchcraft and even the relative merits of Virginian and English tobacco. In the last instance the Government received the answer it wanted — namely, that Virginian was the better — and this, of course, was fortunate since the Government was then anxious to protect colonial interests.

Sir George said that ever since history began the vendors of medicines have peddled their wares and one of the most frustrating tasks that the College ever took upon itself was that of trying to control prescribing. A fellow of the College in the sixteenth or seventeenth century had described the physician as the king of the sick. But this was not necessarily the view of the surgeon, the apothecary or yet of the quack — and in the time of Queen Anne the apothecary won the prior right of prescription. Another field in which the College met with only limited success was the control of the quality of medical literature. It was able to impose a censorship on its fellows but could only criticize outsiders. In the late eighteenth century Heberden tried to establish a standard of medical writing by the direct example of publishing the College transactions — but unfortunately only a few volumes appeared.

By the end of the eighteenth century population and fashion had moved westward from the city, where only a minority of fellows of the College continued to practice, and it was believed that the College should follow this trend. Permission was obtained to hold meetings and exercise its powers within the city of Westminster, and the fourth College was opened at Pall Mall East in 1825. The founding of London University in 1832 and the Medical Act of 1858, which led to the formation of the General Medical Council, changed the function of the College. It lost its licensing power, but at the same time it gained in prestige and took on the function of an examining body, and Sir George thought that the scrupulous impartiality of the censors was reflected in the case of the unsuccessful candidate who challenged the censor to a duel for failing him, was taken to law, but allowed to take the examination again and was admitted as a licentiate. Sir George admitted that sometimes in its history the College has been too rigid, too exclusive or too inactive. But he found no evidence that it had ever deliberately failed to uphold the honor of the physician's art or of his place in society.

The latest move to Regent's Park, which required yet another act of Parliament to allow the College to leave the city of Westminster, was necessitated by the increase in the number of the fellows and members and by increasing scientific activities.

The architect, Mr. Denys Lasdun, who spoke after Sir George Clark, admitted that the new building is modern, and although he had read that some had found the style disturbing, he was glad that there were more who found it exciting. He pointed out that architecture involves space, light, materials and people, and he had tried to use all these to their best advantage. He had studied the history of the College and appreciated the tradition and ritual that gave it its character. He was glad he had been able to let a stone from Linacre's house, which was rebuilt after the Great Fire, into the wall of the new building. He had tried to make the censor's room, which was panelled with the same Spanish oak that adorned the rooms at Warwick Lane and Pall Mall East, the focal point of the building, and the historical portraits had been hung to better advantage than ever before. He hoped that in time all those who used the building would grow to like it. Certainly, it should be a place where the College can fittingly pursue its two continuing concerns — the maintenance of standards of medicine and the encouragement of friendship among physicians.

Holiday Reflections

A peripatetic post with thoughts on many problems, most of which are still with us.

Not so long ago, I was pleased to meet an English medical student who subscribes to the *Journal*. I was glad to hear him speak well of it, and flattered to learn that he reads the London Post to find out what is going on in Britain. I was somewhat dismayed, however, when he asked me, "What is the source of your information?" I replied that I just keep my eyes and ears open and always hope that something relevant will turn up each month.

This was perhaps an oversimplification, because I suppose I do have something of an obsession in the way in which I scan the journals and the newspapers in search of suitable material, and I also try to make a mental and sometimes a written note of the odd remarks, heard on radio or television or even at medical meetings or in daily conversation, that might be turned to the advantage of the Post. Indeed, some of my friends are now aware of my eccentricity in this direction and no longer think it strange when they see me make notes in quite unusual circumstances. On one such recent occasion, I noticed a colleague smile knowingly as I began making notes while a good-looking Indian woman anesthetist was addressing a meeting on postgraduate medical education. She was describing the peculiar problems she had encountered as a foreign medical graduate striving to become an anesthetist while she had a young child and a husband who was training to become an architect, for whom she had to provide a home. I never found an appropriate opportunity for passing on her remarks, but it is perhaps worth mentioning now that she made the comment that the best of the foreign medical graduates who come to Britain and fail to establish themselves tend to emigrate farther west to North America.

But it is my obsession with the newspapers that is rather unpopular at home since none may be put out with the rubbish or for recycling until each one has been gone through and suitable clippings have been taken. Some weeks yield much, and others little of medical interest, and clippings not immediately used are filed away in a folder marked "Material for N.E.J.M." And this really brings me to my point: for several months now the medical and political news has been somber, with a plethora of depressing newspaper reports about the unrest that has been affecting so many groups of workers in the hospitals. There have been reports of strikes, and of threats to private practice, and even of fears for the future viability of National Health Service in its present form. Fortunately, the traditional holiday season in August has brought a temporary respite, and when I went up to Scotland for my own holiday, I brought my folder of clippings with me to see what other topics had been of public interest during these last troubled months. But as I went through them, I was reminded of an intern with whom I once had a minor contretemps. We were making rounds one day when I realized that I remembered more about the patients than he did. When I pointed this out, he said that he believed the trouble was that he remembered the things that interested him, whereas I remembered the things that interested me. When asked about the things that interested him, he explained that his interest was in anything academic. I acknowledged the importance of the academic aspects of medicine, but assured him that my patients were more immediately interested in the practical aspects of their illnesses and had three urgent questions in mind: "What is the diagnosis? What is the treatment? and How soon do I get better?" The intern assured me that, given time, he would be all right. And indeed he was. He married into an academic family, quickly obtained his specialist qualifications and was appointed to a post in a metabolic unit.

No doubt the story is an adverse reflection as much upon myself as upon the intern, and it certainly made me realize how easy it is to concentrate too much on one's own interests. I fear, therefore, that the assorted collection of clippings that I found in my file reflects this weakness in myself and would provide excellent material for any analyst whom I might consult. Nevertheless, many of the references to various aspects of clinical practice are of general interest. Thus, I found several about the bedside manner and the doctor-patient relation. In one, Sir Derrick Dunlop, lately chairman of the Medicines Commission, suggested that the bedside manner is an intangible art, rooted in personality and character, but without which satisfactory relations in clinical medicine are impossible. Its essence is the art of communication with patients, which endows them with the authority that they crave. In another old clipping I found similar remarks by Professor Sir Michael Woodruff, of Edinburgh University. He recognized that in modern medicine there is likely to be a team of doctors, nurses and ancillary workers concerned in the treatment of most patients. He urged, however, that there should be one doctor who is in charge of the patient and who accepts the final responsibility for his management. This would normally be the family doctor chosen by the patient, who then might be referred to a specialist, who in turn might seek the advice of others. But Sir Michael pointed out that this traditional pattern can easily be lost sight of in the National Health Service, and patients attending their doctors' offices may see several different doctors on successive visits. It was encouraging, therefore, to find a report that Professor Pat Byrne, director of the University Department of General Practice at Manchester, is carrying out an investigation into the bedside manner of family doctors. Research workers will record bedside interviews and office consultations to determine whether the qualities of a good doctor could be taught formally to medical students. Present methods of training family physicians have certainly been criticized, and in a report of the Royal Society of Health Congress last year, it was suggested that the organization of family practice requires intensive research. Many family doctors who previously held open office (or "surgery") hours, have introduced appointments systems in the hope that they would be able to see about 12 patients in an hour, but it has been suggested that before introducing such systems, it would have been better to determine how family doctors could get the most out of a consultation of five or 10 minutes. The employment of nurses and receptionists has also greatly changed the character of the family doctor's office. They can assist the doctors by sorting requests for consultations and house calls, but there have been complaints that they sometimes intervene as a barrier between the patient and the doctor.

Certainly, it is clear that many patients are beginning to take a rather cynical view of some of these developments. Thus, there was a lively correspondence in the *Observer* earlier this year under the general title of "doctors versus patients" and another crop of letters appeared more recently in *The Times* on the patient-doctor relation. This series began when a professor, of an undisclosed faculty, complained of his own experience after criticizing his doctor's clinical judgment. He had acquired a painful orthopedic condition for which his doctor referred him to a local specialist. The treatment prescribed appeared to aggravate rather than to relieve the pain, and when he explained this fact to his doctor on the telephone, he was referred to a local hospital for treatment without further examination. At this stage he asked for a second orthopedic opinion, which led to an alternative diagnosis and different treatment, which was immediately effective. While recovering in the hospital, he was requested by his family doctor to re-move himself and his family from the group-practice list on which they were registered and he was duly discharged from the hospital without a family doctor. He suspected that he had been victimized because of some special relation between the local hospital consultants and the family doctors transcending that between patients and their doctors, and wondered what redress a patient might expect in case of unsatisfactory medical attention. He was concerned at the lack of any criteria of relative competence among doctors and thought that the aura of infallibility with which the medical profession seems to sur-round itself should be destroyed. Several long letters followed — some from doctors doing their best to justify the apparent shortcomings of the profession by emphasizing the difficulties presented by the unlimited demands of patients, others ex-plaining that some system of medical audit and peer review might well be introduced, and still others assuring the profes-sor that the Department of Health is busy setting up Commu-nity Health Councils, which will have some responsibility for monitoring the quality of health care.

Fortunately, these are all matters to which the profession is in fact alert, and the whole question of the competence of doctors to practice will be pronounced upon when the Merri-son Committee reports later this year on the future role of the General Medical Council, which is responsible for the regula-tion of the profession. One particularly difficult subject on which this Committee will need to advise is the "Worry of the Sick, leading the Sick," as another of my clippings describes the problem of the doctor who is mentally or physically ill but still remains in practice. Unfortunately, we do not seem to be a very stable group: statistics show that doctors in Britain have nearly twice the suicide rate of the rest of the population, and their wives are also apt to take their lives. Drug dependence has been estimated to be at least 30 times that of the general population, and there is a widely held assumption that doctors are likely to become alcoholics. The stresses involved in medical practice have been blamed for these misfortunes, but the alcoholic doctor is no new phenomenon, as I discovered while re-reading *Mutiny on the Bounty*. For it is recorded there that on December 9, 1788, the surgeon of the *Bounty* died from the effects of intemperance and indolence. This unfortunate man had been in a constant state of intoxication and was so averse to any kind of exercise that he could never be prevailed on to take half a dozen hours on the deck at a time in the course of the voyage.

And so, to prevent myself from degenerating into such an unhappy state, I must put away my papers and resume my holiday exercise on the golf course, where in fact one of my clippings reminds me that I may also have the opportunity of observing nature, which might help to maintain my own competence to practice. But, of course, that would not help my golf — so I had better try to keep my eyes on the ball.

Bicentennial Greetings

JULY 29, 1976

It would have been hard to find a more appropriate or more delightful venue for an Anglo-American meeting than Leeds Castle. The proceedings of the symposium, held to celebrate the American Bicentennial, have been published by the Macy Foundation (Bowers JZ, Purcell EF, eds. The university and medicine: the past — the present — and tomorrow. New York: Josiah Macy, Jr., Foundation, 1977).

It was a privilege to participate recently in an Anglo-American bicentennial discussion arranged by the Josiah Macy, Jr., Foundation. The theme was "The University and Medicine," the past, present and tomorrow, and the venue was Leeds Castle, near Maidstone in Kent.

The choice of Leeds Castle was appropriate in view of its rather remarkable Anglo-American associations. The long history of this beautifully situated castle dates back to Saxon times, when Leed, Chief Minister to Ethelbert II of Kent, built a wooden castle on two islands on a lake formed by the river Len. After the invasion by William the Conqueror it passed into the hands of powerful Norman barons, who rebuilt the castle in stone in 1119 and retained it in their family until Edward I took it over in 1272, after which it remained a royal castle for 300 years.

Henry VIII was the most famous of all its owners and carried out extensive additions and improvements. It was then given to Sir Anthony St. Leger by Edward VI as a reward for governing Ireland successfully by means of a conciliatory policy and persuading the Irish to accept the English King as King of Ireland. Unfortunately, Sir Anthony's grandson ruined himself by giving financial backing to Sir Walter Raleigh's ill-fated expedition to Eldorado, and the castle passed into the ownership of Lord Culpepper, Chancellor of the Exchequer and Master of the Rolls, who was also made Lord Proprietor of 5,200,000 acres of Virginia and Maryland by Charles II. Eventually, the fifth Lord Fairfax married the Culpepper heiress and succeeded to Leeds Castle and these great American estates. The sixth Lord Fairfax emigrated to America to develop the estates and became the friend and patron of the young George Washington, who was then a surveyor. Lord Fairfax gave him the task of laying out a new town in the Shenandoah valley, and as a result of the friendship that the two men established, Fairfax was unmolested by the rebels during the Revolutionary War and even allowed to keep his personal property, which then extended to about 300,000 acres.

This interesting Anglo-American association of Leeds Castle was renewed when the Hon. Olive Lady Baillie became the owner in 1926. Having an American mother, Pauline Whitney, and an English father, Lord Queensborough, she was always anxious to foster good Anglo-American relations, and before she died in 1974, she had made arrangements to ensure that the castle should be preserved for the public benefit. And so under the terms of her will a charitable foundation has been established, one of the main provisions being that facilities should be provided for the pursuit of active medical research work based primarily on the co-operation of American and British medical scientists.

The recent meeting was the first Anglo-American venture to be held at the castle; the proceedings of this small bicentennial discussion group will be published in due course.

It was of great interest to reflect on the state of medicine and the universities in the year 1776 and then to try to see how the universities, the science of medicine, and the pattern of medical education and medical care evolved in the two countries over the two centuries that followed. In the second half of the 18th century medical advances depended on deductions made from chance observations — often by country folk. Thus, Edward Jenner and William Withering were both provincial practitioners, and both received the inspiration for their discoveries from folk medicine. Withering stated that it was in 1775 that he learned that the country folk of Shropshire were using foxglove tea as a cure for dropsy, though it was not until 1783 that digitalis made its first official appearance in the Edinburgh pharmacopoeia.

Jenner too spent 20 years considering the statement of the Gloucestershire dairymaid that "I can't take smallpox, for I have already had cowpox." Then, in 1796, he vaccinated an eight-year-old boy with pus from the hand of a dairymaid who had become infected with cowpox. Eight weeks later he inoculated the boy with smallpox, and no disease appeared. It is interesting that it has taken nearly 200 years to rid the world of smallpox.

In my room at Leeds Castle there was a copy of Trevelyan's *History of England*. Seeking reference to the time of independence, I was interested to read, that

. . . the general causes rendering it difficult for the English and the Americans to understand one another were then numerous and profound. Many have been removed by the passage of time. English society was still aristocratic while American society was already democratic. Six or seven weeks of disagreeable ocean tossing divided London from Boston so that personal intercourse was slight and the stream of emigration had run very dry ever since 1640.

It says much for the stamina of the doctors of that time that they were quite prepared to face the ocean tossing to visit

Europe for medical training, the majority going to Edinburgh where the Medical School had been founded in 1726. Indeed, the remarkably close association between Edinburgh and America, and Philadelphia in particular, is reflected in such names as John Morgan, William Shippen and Benjamin Rush, all of whom studied in Edinburgh before achieving distinction in the new University of Pennsylvania.

The place of John Fothergill at that time is also of great interest. Born in Yorkshire in 1718 and also receiving his medical education in Edinburgh, he settled in London, where he acquired a large practice. He became a close friend of Benjamin Franklin during the American's long visits to England and collaborated with him in trying to prevent the break between England and the American colonies. Although unsuccessful, Fothergill is remembered as a friend of America. It may be recalled that he became a great expert in botany; it is perhaps of Anglo-American interest that he popularized the use of coffee, promoted its cultivation in the West Indies and wrote a paper entitled "History and Use of Coffee."

During the 18th century there was much activity in hospital building in both Britain and America. Indeed, in Britain no less than 154 new hospitals and dispensaries were established between 1700 and 1825, including Guy's, Westminster, the London and the Middlesex hospitals; St. Bartholomew's and St. Thomas's were founded much earlier. Great medical and teaching traditions grew up around these hospitals, but unlike Edinburgh, where the Medical School had been part of the university since 1726, these London schools were independent, for the University of London was not established until 1836.

After the Declaration of Independence there was a distinct decline in the previous reliance of the American colleges on the established British universities, and American university education rapidly expanded. During the 19th and early 20th centuries the concept of the university with its provisions of higher educational opportunity and its concern to advance, preserve and transmit knowledge received much popular support in both countries. On the other hand, it does seem that in recent years there has been some tendency for the relation between the universities and society to deteriorate. The reasons for this development are complex, but it must be due in part to changing social conditions.

In the training of doctors there are problems in the relations between the medical schools and the universities; in constructing the curriculum it is necessary to take account not only of the great scientific advances of recent years but also of the changes taking place in society. Thus, the modern medical student certainly requires adequate training in the basic sciences, but in Britain there is increasing pressure to introduce teaching on topics related to the social and community responsibilities of the physician. This responsibility is being added partly because the role of the priest has declined, partly because the decisions of doctors carry important financial implications (a relevant consideration whether the cost is being borne by the state, an insurance carrier or an individual), and partly because in Britain there is a shift in emphasis away from the acute hospital, with more emphasis on the care of the patient within the community. This development may be relevant and appropriate, but those involved in teaching must surely continue to teach what is best for the patient, who can so easily take second place to some scientific exercise or to some official policy. Thus, although we must be grateful for the scientific advances of the last two centuries, we must also ensure that medicine remains an art that takes full advantage of these advances but is not displaced by them.

Furthermore, we must ensure that even though in every developed country the responsibility for the provision of health care is passing into the hands of the politicians, the independence of our profession is preserved. This end will be achieved only if we maintain our own professional standards.

In offering these bicentennial thoughts and greetings, which were inspired by the Leeds Castle meeting, I hope that the long tradition of Anglo-American co-operation in the field of medicine and science will continue and that medical men and women will continue to cross the Atlantic in both directions. The age of jet aircraft has spared us those days or weeks of ocean tossing, and in spite of its alleged noisy pollution Lord Fairfax would doubtless have been proud to see Concorde descend over his Virginian acres!

I am indebted to the Rt. Hon. Lord Geoffrey Lloyd, chairman of the Leeds Castle Charitable Trust, for the historical details of the Castle, and to Dr. John Z. Bowers for permission to refer to the Macy Foundation meeting before publication of the proceedings.

Uniformity versus Diversity in Medical Care

JULY 28, 1977

The concept of providing a comprehensive health service that is freely available to every citizen at the time of need is clearly attractive. The legislation that led to the introduction of such a service in Britain in 1948 was widely regarded as socially just.

The National Health Service has ensured that there is a uniform standard of care throughout the country. This is in marked contrast to the situation in many other countries, where there is both a diversity of methods of health-care delivery and a variation in standards. It is interesting to consider whether uniformity must inevitably lead to mediocrity.

On a recent visit to the United States one of my tasks was to speak about health care in Britain today at a symposium on the wider topic of world health care. While preparing my presentation, I found myself recalling the serious problems that have confronted the National Health Service (NHS) in the last few years, and I realized that many of the political decisions that have greatly changed the character of the health service could be justified in the light of the conditions prevailing at the time they were taken.

Thus, the controversial reorganization of the NHS in 1974 could be justified on the grounds that it was logical to unify the management of the hospitals, the family-practitioner service and the community health services. It was also right to try to improve the administration of the NHS at the time it was reorganized, and it is unfortunate that the new administrative structure adopted has caused decision making to become slower and more difficult rather than quicker and easier, as was intended.

The attack on private practice was clearly more difficult to justify. On the other hand, although this attack was motivated by political dogma, the politicians could argue that the rise of professionalism and trade-unionism among members of the allied health services and their intense dislike of any private practice within the NHS made it necessary to separate private practice from the NHS to appease these essential health-care workers.

Escalating costs and financial stringency have justified more recent political decisions. Thus, it was right that priorities should be identified and means found to achieve a more even distribution of resources throughout the country. It is not surprising that studies revealed that the areas of greatest need were in the care of the young and the old, the mentally ill and the handicapped, and that communities clustered around university centers were receiving relatively more per capita for medical care than those farther away from such centers of excellence.

In the light of such findings it was logical for the politicians, who are concerned with issues affecting population groups, in contrast to physicians, who are concerned with individual patients, to decide to divert public spending toward these areas of need and to redistribute the total available resources on a more nearly equitable basis. It was also logical, on the assumption that the care of the patient within the community is often more appropriate, and certainly cheaper, than in the hospital, for the politicians to support the continuing development of primary-care services and to encourage outpatient investigations and treatment in preference to supporting more expensive hospital-based medicine. All such measures that have been implemented in Britain may have been justified in the light of escalating costs, financial crisis and political pressures, but in a subtle way they have led to radical changes in the character of the health service.

Thus, a service that initially retained considerable diversity is now becoming steadily more uniform, with diminishing opportunities for choice by patients and increasing limitations on the freedom of practice by the medical profession. Not only does the state decide the global sum that will be available for the NHS and how it will be distributed throughout the country, but it also decides the way in which medical care will be delivered to those in need. The danger seems to be that the public may ultimately become conditioned to accept the health service that the state sees fit to provide (or decides that it can afford to provide), with virtually no choice and no chance to check on standards.

Other speakers in the symposium on world health care spoke about the development of fully socialized medicine in such countries as the Soviet Union and Sweden. There seems to be no doubt that the uniformity of these systems carries with it the threat of mediocrity. In Sweden in particular, patients complain of the lack of continuity of medical care and the lack of any choice of physician, but it was interesting to learn that some element of choice is being restored there with the renaissance of a private sector outside the state system.

In contrast to these health-care systems, which are becoming increasingly uniform, the system in the United States remains diverse, and it was encouraging to learn, from those speaking about the American system, of the improvement in health statistics over the past few years, particularly those relating to age-adjusted death rates, infant mortality and the accessibility of medical care to the poorer sectors of society. The great contributions of the Medicare and Medicaid programs in making health care available to the elderly and the poor were acknowledged, and it was recognized that if the other sectors of the health-care system are to remain free of more direct control, the medical profession must act as a responsible service profession. But one speaker did emphasize the need to differentiate health care from medical care, which he did not consider to be synonymous. He regarded medical care as being concerned with the detection of the presence or absence of disease and with its treatment when present. This detection was the direct responsibility of the doctors, but wider issues of health care were the responsibility of government. Although doctors must advise on matters concerning preventive medicine and environmental health, they should not be held responsible for deficiencies that only governments could remedy.

But, as in all other developed countries, the escalating costs of medical care in the United States and the inevitable intervention of the government in assisting those unable to provide for themselves are being matched by a tendency to greater control over the way public money is spent and a consequent trend toward uniformity rather than diversity.

Meanwhile, however, it is interesting for a visitor from a country with an increasingly uniform system of medical care to see the varying types of practice in different parts of the United States. Certainly, the increasing emphasis on primary care is evident. I particularly enjoyed a seminar for members of a family-practice faculty, which was being conducted by an emigrant member of the Royal College of General Practitioners. Again, I was pleased to make rounds with the residents in another department of family practice and to learn that several of them were planning to practice in rural areas, though unlike their British family-practitioner counterparts, they would naturally expect to have full bed privileges in their local hospitals. It was also instructive to visit a community health center in the suburbs of a busy Southern city, where a competent nurse practitioner was rendering primary care in accordance with the protocols laid down. Any prejudice against such a system was dispelled by this visit.

But apart from the diversity of the medical-care system in the United States it is the remarkable wealth of facilities that is so impressive for the visiting physician, though I detected a growing concern that in some cases, these facilities are becoming unnecessarily extravagant and that more selectivity is required in their use. I found it refreshing, therefore, to hear a young physician, at grand rounds in a large hospital, express his concern on such matters. In a paper, supported by facts and figures, he argued against the routine use of intravenous pyelography in the investigation of hypertension on the grounds that its value did not justify the cost. He pointed out that renovascular hypertension accounts for no more than 5 per cent of all cases of hypertension and that even in this group there may be more false-negative than true-positive pyelographic findings. He emphasized that careful history taking and clinical examination should identify the cases in which the procedure is indicated.

It is perhaps strange that in our rigid system in Britain, we have been spared any statutory requirement to carry out medical audit or to establish bed-utilization review committees. In fact, in the British system there is at present too little incentive to be cost conscious, since no personal benefit to the physician, or indeed to the local hospital, results from local economies. Of course, in Britain we already work with modest resources, and there may be some merit in the principle of providing the minimum requirements to meet any particular need. On the other hand, the merit of the more diverse American system is that it allows competition, innovation and experiment, though it carries the risk that too many unevenly distributed facilities will be created, so that if the system is to be protected from excessive central control, it is clearly important to ensure that these facilities are properly used.

On reflection I believe that there is much to be learned from study of both types of system and that more opportunities should be available for students, residents and also more senior practitioners to have opportunities for exchange visits.

It was encouraging to meet American students who had visited Britain and to learn that they had been stimulated by the traditional clinical approach of the British physician — who still carries out fewer investigations than his American counterpart — and to meet teachers of family practice and organizers of postgraduate and continuing-education programs who had visited family-practice teaching programs and postgraduate institutes in Britain and found these visits worthwhile. Such exchanges should be encouraged in both directions. It must be hoped that whatever steps our governments may take to control the immigration of medical manpower, they will do nothing to stand in the way of these well established practices, particularly among the young, for the onus will be upon them to ensure that state intervention in health-care delivery will not necessarily lead to excessive uniformity and so to mediocrity.

A Visit of Exploration

JANUARY 26, 1978

In the autumn of 1977 I was asked to make a visit of exploration to Australia on behalf of the King Edward VII Hospital Fund for London. The particular objective was to study the Australian health-care system and to identify hospitals and other scientific institutions in Australia where British medical graduates might profitably spend some time in undertaking postgraduate training or research.

Although it is a few years since I made this visit to Australia, it nevertheless seemed worthwhile to include this review of my impressions at the time. Since 1977 a number of changes have taken place, and the Medibank system has been considerably modified.

I have to confess that the title of last month's contribution to this column ("Backward or Forward?") could not have been more appropriate from a personal point of view because it was written as I made the journey from London to Sydney by the trans-Pacific route. During this westward journey halfway around the world my watch had, of course, been set back 12 hours and then put forward 24 hours when we crossed the international date line, so that I was not sure myself whether I was going backward or forward and hope that this state of personal confusion was not too apparent to those who may have read my remarks.

The purpose of this long journey was to make a visit of exploration on behalf of the King Edward VII Hospital Fund for London, with the particular objective of studying the health-care system and trying to identify hospitals and other scientific institutions in Australia where British medical graduates might profitably spend some time in undertaking postgraduate training or research. This was a formidable task to attempt in four weeks since it involved visiting all the major cities with the exception of Hobart in Tasmania, but it proved to be a rewarding experience. In this rather personal Post I share my observations with readers of the *Journal*, since they may well be of relevance to American as well as to British doctors.

It would obviously be improper to try to reach any firm conclusions about the effectiveness of the health-care delivery service or the overall standards of medicine in a country on the basis of a short visit, but having met a large number of practicing doctors in every branch of medicine and surgery and visited all the medical schools and many hospitals in Sydney, Melbourne, Brisbane, Adelaide and Perth, as well as the new medical school in Newcastle, New South Wales, I can at least make a broad assessment of the situation and offer suggestions about the primary objective of the visit.

For someone arriving on the Australian medical scene from Britain, the immediate cultural shock is the discovery that medicine is based almost entirely on the fee-for-item-of-service system, with everyone being insured either through the federally controlled Medibank system or through private insurance schemes. Although at first this setup may not appear very different from the American system it does seem that the pattern of medicine and the image of the doctor in Australia have undergone considerable change since Medibank was introduced. Before Medibank doctors were highly regarded in Australia, but their campaign against its introduction by the Whitlam government seems to have been ill conceived and harmed their image, for it made them appear to be resistant to the altruistic objective of making good health care more generally available. Their resistance seems to have been based on the fear that even though the principle of fee for item of service was to be preserved, the fact that these fees would come from government sources was a threat to the independence of the profession and carried the risk that a British type of National Health Service would be imposed at a later date.

After the return of the Liberal government, modifications were made in Medibank; the independence of the profession has not been seriously challenged, and the fee-for-item-of-service system has enabled many practitioners to acquire large gross earnings. General practitioners and surgeons in private practice are among the high earners, but it is in pathology that the fee-for-item-of-service system has made it possible for really high incomes to be made. Radiology offers a similar opportunity, and the proliferation of CAT scanners with too little monitoring of their use is viewed with the same concern as in the United States. But in the academic units in university hospitals the situation is very different. Professors and senior lecturers are paid salaries that were regarded as reasonable before the introduction of Medibank and before inflation took its toll but are now only barely adequate. Even with the 25 per cent addition to their salaries that they are permitted to earn in private practice, their earnings compare most unfavorably with those of their colleagues in private practice. Nor is this their only worry. They fear that the present situation is altering the attitude of doctors to their profession, changing the character of hospital practice and adversely affecting recruitment to academic posts and the teaching of undergraduate and post-graduate students.

Thus, in Australia as in Britain, the residents have demanded, and have been granted, a basic working week varying from 40 to 48 hours, with additional pay for on-call duties that often enables them to earn more than their seniors on the hospital staff. Doubtless, many are well motivated, and there is increasing interest among young graduates in the developing family-practice programs, but there are also many who seek specialist recognition as early as possible with a view to entering the lucrative field of private medical or surgical practice. This emphasis on the private sector has implications both for medical education and for the staffing of public hospitals. Thus, with about 70 per cent of all surgical procedures being carried out in private hospitals and most outpatient consultations taking place in doctors' private offices rather than in hospital clinics, students and residents are being denied access to much valuable clinical experience. Similarly, because pathologists and radiologists can earn so much in private practice, many are spending most of their time in their private laboratories, and many smaller hospitals are having difficulty in staffing their laboratory and radiology departments — some have had to enter into contracts with private laboratory services.

Another cause of worry is the fact that in some areas, recognized specialists, particularly surgeons, are practicing entirely in private hospitals, without any public-hospital or teaching-hospital affiliation. There was no suggestion that the standard of such private medicine is not high, but there was anxiety that it is often unchecked medicine because the records system in most private hospitals is inadequate. Although the rates of appendicectomy, cholecystectomy and hysterectomy tend to be high in private practice, there are rarely any facilities for tissue audit in private hospitals.

Having had this general background explained, and having had it stressed that the situation may vary in detail from one state to another, I was reassured to find that in many parts of Australia, there are active research institutes that have world-wide reputations and offer unrivaled opportunities. Similarly, there are many teaching hospitals where excellent medicine and surgery are being practiced and where any young doctor would benefit from a period of postgraduate training.

It was also interesting to visit community hospitals away from the main centers, and to see how they are participating both in undergraduate and in postgraduate education. Thus, the staff of many of these hospitals, apart from providing an efficient service for the local community, are developing links with teaching hospitals and establishing rotating residency training programs and accepting students for part of their clinical training. This trend, which is similar to that in Britain, is welcomed by the teaching hospitals, where the clinical material, already in short supply, is likely to be seriously inadequate for the increasing numbers of medical students being admitted to medical schools.

This increase in medical-school intake is a particularly controversial issue; there seems to be the same lack of informed opinion in Australia about the number of doctors who should be trained as exists in other countries. Furthermore, as in Britain and North America, the manpower situation is complicated by medical immigration. Thus, for many years there has been a steady flow of doctors into Australia from Britain, and more recently there have been increasing numbers of immigrants from South Africa, Rhodesia and Asia. For all these reasons there is a firm belief that before long Australia may have too many doctors and a growing conviction that a more selective policy concerning immigration of doctors will be required, with a further restriction on the reciprocal recognition of overseas medical qualifications.

The role of women in medicine is also a matter for debate. The proportion of women medical students continues to rise, but the fact that many of them are unlikely to engage in full-time practice is recognized as one factor that may reduce the effect on medical manpower of increasing the number of medical students.

I was interested to visit the newer medical schools of Monash in Victoria and Flinders in South Australia and to see how the modified integrated curriculum operated by both these medical schools is developing. In Newcastle, New South Wales, a new medical school is preparing for its first intake of

60 students with a faculty of progressive academics who are planning an ambitious integrated program based on the concept of trying to alert students to their basic medical task of problem solving from the beginning of their training. It will be interesting to see how the project develops. In the field of postgraduate training the specialist colleges in Australia have been active in site visiting and in accrediting training programs, as in Britain and in the United States, and there are the same misgivings as in Britain because, although flexibility is advocated in the planning of training programs, they increasingly tend to become too rigid.

I also found considerable interest in the continuing-education programs that have been developing in Britain, particularly the inducements offered to encourage practitioners to attend. There was some surprise when I explained that the requirement that British family doctors had to attend a specified number of postgraduate sessions each year to qualify for their seniority payments has been withdrawn. It is too early to assess the effect of this modification on attendances at postgraduate courses in Britain. In any event, the problem of providing continuing education for family doctors in Australia is quite different from that in Britain, as a professor of family medicine pointed out when he challenged me to tell him how I would update a single-handed family physician practicing 3000 km north of Perth in Western Australia who was unable to obtain a locum to allow him to leave his practice.

However, apart from such special problems related to the geographic and demographic features of the country, the topics that Australian colleagues wished to discuss were those familiar to doctors in both Britain and the United States. Yet it was disturbing to find that many senior members of the medical profession in Australia are seriously troubled that the ethos of the profession is suffering because too many doctors are becoming preoccupied with the financial rewards of medicine and with the responsibilities of high incomes. This attitude was confusing for a visitor from Britain who has always believed both in the principles of the National Health Service and in the need for a strong private sector in medicine. The Australian scene contrasts strangely with the present situation in British hospitals, where many consultants have become demoralized because of their low rates of pay and because of the political attack on private practice. The lesson to be learned from this paradox seems to be that doctors should be fairly paid and that their professional standards may suffer if their earnings are either unreasonably high or unacceptably low. But, of course, the determination of fair pay remains the crucial problem — and one that no country seems to have solved satisfactorily. In Britain the Independent Review Body on Doctors' Pay was accepted as a fair arbitrator until its independence was compromised by the government's instruction to the chairman to take account of the current economic situation when making his recommendations, followed by its refusal to implement them because of the prevailing national wage policy.

I must return to consider the value of encouraging British, or perhaps American, graduates to spend a period in medical research or postgraduate education in Australia. Because of their small population and isolated position, many Australian doctors have regarded it as a necessary part of their training to spend a year abroad, usually in Britain or America. From my discussions I formed the impression that Australia would welcome advanced trainees coming in the reverse direction for a limited time in larger numbers than do so at present. There are certainly many centers of excellence where special skills could be acquired, and others where research projects could be pursued. And even in less specialized units, the exchange of views and the experience of working with different people in a different environment would provide valuable if not easily measurable benefits. For these reasons I believe that efforts should be made to facilitate the short-term interchange of young doctors between such countries as Australia, Britain and the United

States, particularly at present, when circumstances relating to different training and licensure requirements and medical-manpower problems are making such visits more difficult than previously.

My four weeks in Australia have certainly taught me a great deal. I hope that the benefit may have been mutual, that I am not wildly wrong in my observations and deductions and that my remarks will not offend any of my many kind hosts.

An Expedition to Bath

As the last paragraph reveals, my companion on this visit to Bath was Dr. Franz Ingelfinger. Although far from well, he was making a trip to Europe to receive an honor from his German colleagues in gastroenterology. He was very keen to visit Bath since he was hoping to write a book about spas. It was late September, the weather was glorious, and I believe that Franz greatly enjoyed the visit. He was fascinated with the statistics about the hotwater spring but frustrated that we could not bathe.

I am quite accustomed to arranging programs for visiting professors on sabbatical leave or for students wishing to undertake elective periods of study, but a recent request was more unusual. An old friend from the United States wrote to say that he was planning a trip to Europe and was anxious to make a visit to Bath since he had an interest in spas, and he wondered whether I should care to join him. Having accepted the invitation, I began to wonder how to play my part in making the visit a success. Fortunately, I remembered that a colleague had close connections with Bath, and through his good offices, we were asked to begin our visit by calling on one of the physicians at his home on the beautiful Royal Crescent. There, we learned the history of the waters and the benefit that they had conferred on patients and on the city itself, and we were presented with a small book entitled *Bath Water*.[1]

Before long we were on a visit to the hospital, which was followed by a conducted tour of the Roman baths, where we were able to test the temperature of the water, but not able to bathe! The story of the city is told in the book we had been given, which describes how Bath is Britain's only hot-water spa. Because of a fault in the volcanic structure of the earth's crust there is a spring that delivers half a millon gallons (1,890,000 liters) of water every day at a temperature of 120° F (49° C) from strata some 5000 feet (1500 meters) below ground level. The water has a low mineral content and it is slightly radioactive (1.7 nCi of radon per liter).

The Romans built elegant baths over the swamp on which the city was situated, but after they left, there was a period of decay until a Saxon revival culminating in the crowning of King Edgar in Bath Abbey in 973. But, later, the city was visited by pestilence and fire and then remained a quiet market and wool town until the 18th century, when its waters became popular for their alleged healing properties, and the city became a fashionable retreat for wealthy invalids who came not only for treatment but because, in the season, Bath had become the focal point for English Society. Indeed, George II and Queen Charlotte were frequent visitors to the city, and Pope, Defoe, Smollett, Gainsborough, Samuel Johnson, Boswell, Horace Walpole, Jane Austen and Sheridan were others who either lived in Bath or visited the city regularly.

Not surprisingly, the medical profession in the city has flourished, and many of the doctors have been eminent. The Bath Hospital was opened in 1742, and the first physician was Dr. William Oliver, who was a fellow of the Royal Society and also the originator of the recipe for the Bath Oliver biscuit, which acquired a worldwide reputation. Perhaps medically more important was the relationship that he established with his surgical colleagues, which is commemorated in a painting still hanging on the stairs of the hospital in which Dr. Oliver is shown consulting with Mr. Pierce, an orthopedic surgeon, about the management of three patients, one with rheumatoid arthritis, another probably with lead palsy and the third possibly with leprosy. In 1887 the name of the hospital was changed to the Royal Mineral Water Hospital, and in 1935, by Act of Parliament, the name became the Royal National Hospital for Rheumatic Disease. From that time the staff of the hospital has been engaged in active research into the causation and management of rheumatic disorders and has continued to take full advantage of the spa waters in developing hydrotherapy programs.

The modern approach to the treatment of rheumatism has dispelled the folklore of the healing waters, but *Bath Water* points out that a spa is a refuge from stress, which doubtless accounts for many of the ills of modern society. Furthermore, the waters have been stated by the cynic to be the only treatment in medicine that has done no harm!

The more the pity that because the National Health Service has withdrawn its support, the city's Hot-Spring Treatment Centre has had to close, and the visiting pilgrim can only look upon the waters in the Roman baths, or get himself admitted to the hospital, and is unable to test for himself the possible beneficial effect of these warm mineral waters.

All the same, it is still worth visiting Bath to see the elegance of the houses built in the 18th century and to set foot on the stones around the baths laid nearly 2000 years ago, especially if one's companion is none other than the emeritus editor of the *Journal*, Dr. Franz Ingelfinger, and one's local guide, Dr. George Kersley, the author of *Bath Water*!

---

1. Kersley GD. Bath water: the effect of the waters on the history of Bath and of medicine. Bath, England: Morgan Books, 1973.

Sustaining the Common Language

It has been said that the United States and Britain are two nations separated by a common language. In this essay an attempt has been made to determine whether this assertion is false or true.

Some months ago it was reported that Mr. Robert Burchfield, the chief editor of the *Oxford English Dictionary*, had said at a press conference[1] in Chicago that in another 200 years, English-speaking Americans and English-speaking Britons will not be able to understand what they are saying to each other. He said that vocabulary, not accent, would be the stumbling block, and he pointed out that the language split began late in the 18th century. Since that time there has been a progressive divergence between British English and American English, and Mr. Burchfield believes that this division will eventually lead to a condition of unintelligibility. Since the great majority of Britons have never visited the United States and the majority of Americans have never visited Britain it is not surprising that the English language should develop differently on each side of the Atlantic, but Mr. Burchfield thinks that part of the responsibility for the language drift must lie with British academics who refuse to have dealings with American English. *The Times*,[2] in an editorial entitled "Anglophones of the Future," recalled how, in the past, loss of contact between speakers of one language led to the development of new languages, so that spoken Latin was transformed into Portuguese, French, Italian and Rumanian after the respective countries were isolated by the collapse of the Roman Empire. *The Times* also recalls the old joke that claims that Britain and the United States are two nations separated by a common language, but it does not welcome the idea of ending any estrangement by the disintegration of the language that keeps us apart. In any case, although it is true that in Britain we do call the elevator the lift, the trunk of the car the boot, the hood the bonnet, the windshield the windscreen and the fenders the wings, the medical profession in both countries seems to strive to make English the first language at international meetings.

Fortunately, many of our colleagues in non-English-speaking countries are better linguists than most Americans and most Britons and often seem willing to accept English as the common language — even though the accent and the vocabulary may both deviate from the standards set by purists such as Burchfield and Webster. But it is perhaps better not to insist upon too uniform a version of English, for surely a variety of both vocabulary and of dialect is more likely to ensure the survival of the basic English language — but perhaps we should just try to watch our grammar!

Nevertheless, during a recent visit to the United States I admit that I believe I was more aware than ever before of this diverging vocabulary, though quite soon I found that I was tending to speak American English myself.

Much more striking to me, however, than our diverging languages was the divergence that seems to be developing between Britain and the United States not only in our health-care delivery systems, but in the field of medical practice. Thus, the contrast in the standard of hospital facilities and medical equipment and in the availability of trained specialists between our two countries is now remarkable. Indeed, many American colleagues found it hard to believe that in Britain, district hospitals serving populations of 200,000 or more would rarely have a full range of specialist services, so that patients requiring investigation with computerized axial tomographic (CAT) scanners, or even ultrasound, would have to be referred to regional centers; and patients requiring neurosurgical or thoracic operations, renal dialysis or radiotherapy would usually be seen by visiting specialists and then transferred to regional centers for treatment.

This situation has arisen partly because the traditional clinical approach so characteristic of British medicine has perhaps made us slow to take full advantage of the modern technology that we have often pioneered, but, of course, the major factor has been the strict regulation of the funding, resources and manpower available to the National Health Service (NHS). Thus there are far fewer specialists in British hospitals than in the United States. Indeed, when I had the privilege of attending the annual clinical congress of the American College of Surgeons in San Francisco and found that more than 12,800 doctors had registered, I realized that this figure was more than the total number of consultants in all hospital specialties employed in the whole of England and Wales. Furthermore, on consulting the latest available figures from the Department of Health and Social Security,[3] I found that there are only 946 general surgeons, 609 orthopedic surgeons, 114 cardiothoracic surgeons, 84 neurosurgeons and 698 gynecologists for a population of nearly 50 million. In the medical specialties there are 1044 internists, 452 pediatricians, 349 geriatricians, 272 chest physicians, 201 rheumatologists, 193 dermatologists, 94 cardiologists and 42 nephrologists, with smaller numbers in the subspecialties.

Now, I am aware that it is a major concern in the United States that there are too many specialists and too many subspecialties, and when I lamented the lack of facilities for CAT scanning, renal dialysis and coronary bypass operations in Britain and mentioned the long waiting lists for elective surgical procedures such as hernia repair and hip replacement, there were some doctors, but more sociologists, who remarked that our mortality indexes and statistics in Britain are still good. This assertion is true, and it is always humbling for physicians to learn that their interventions on behalf of individual patients have much less influence on the accepted indexes of health care than the efforts of those who have worked hard and long to raise the general standards of living and to improve the state of nutrition of the population as a whole.

All the same, although it is sometimes said that death is a good index, it is somewhat final, and there is no doubt that some patients are being denied the benefits of modern medicine in Britain because the total money available to the NHS is being rigidly controlled by the central government.

Thus, although every person in Britain has access to the health-care delivery system through the primary-care or general-practitioner service, without any payment at the time, the benefit of such access is greatly diminished if the real need of the patient cannot be met.

But during my visit to the United States I was, of course, aware of the increasing pressure from politicians and trade unionists for the introduction of some form of national health insurance. This pressure has been generated as the result of concern about the escalating cost of health care and the claim by the politicians in particular that there are many citizens either carrying inadequate health insurance or not being covered at all. Lay friends did assure me that catastrophic illness can cause great hardship, but specific cases were hard to identify, and I was interested to learn the unsolicited views of a working man when I visited a post office to buy airmail stamps. The clerk behind the counter obviously noticed my accent and immediately asked, "You have socialized medicine in Britain, don't you?" I replied that I happened to be a doctor and was interested in his question but wondered why he had asked it. He answered that he had no idea that I was a doctor, but he was interested in the medical system in England because people in the United States go bankrupt when they get sick. I told him that I had heard this statement, but asked him to tell me about his own insurance, and he explained that the Post Office paid 60 per cent of his Blue Cross–Blue Shield insurance and he paid the other 40 per cent himself. When I asked him if he was worried about what would happen if he or his wife became seriously ill, he assured me that he would have no anxiety because he was well covered: he did not just have the low cover — he had the high cover! Anyway, he had been lucky so far and he had not been too ill, but his wife had arthritis and only that morning she had asked him to get her some more pills. She was supposed to take eight a day, but the new supply cost $29, so he had told her they could afford only six a day in the future! All the same he did not want the kind of socialized medicine that there is in Britain, but he did think something should be done about people who cannot afford to insure themselves properly and may go bankrupt when they get sick!

In fact, this was the message that I got from most people to whom I spoke, both lay and medical. It seems to me that it should be possible to make provision for those unable to provide for themselves and to protect everyone from the worst consequences of catastrophic illness without introducing a fully comprehensive state-supported health service modeled on the NHS, which the more radical politicians seem anxious to do. I do not suggest that the NHS has no merits. Indeed, as previously mentioned, the obvious advantage of such a comprehensive system is that everyone needing medical care can have access to it without any anxiety about finance. But when the central government decides how the health-care delivery program shall be constructed, administered and financed, there is danger that decisions will be taken more on grounds of political expediency than in the light of the genuine needs of patients, that some form of rationing will be imposed to contain costs and that eventually a monopoly in health care will develop that will remove freedom of choice from the patients and threaten standards. These trends have all been seen in the NHS and must have an adverse effect on the practice of medicine. For this reason I believe that it is important that the diversity of practice still so apparent in the United States should be preserved. But in contrast to the austerity of the NHS, there are some aspects of the health-care delivery system in the United States that do appear extravagant, even after the cost of the defensive medicine made necessary by the fear of litigation is discounted.

It was encouraging, therefore, to find leaders of the profession urging their colleagues to take the initiative in studying the problems of cost containment, manpower distribution and allocation of resources in the hope that voluntary action may forestall the need for government regulation. As a friendly observer, I can only say that I believe that it is important for the future of American medicine that this hope may be realized. I also hope that our common language will be preserved in an intelligible form and that the style of medical practice in both our countries will continue to bear the mark of the clinical tradition on which both British and American medicine was founded. But, as Mr. Burchfield pointed out, it is only when contact is lost between speakers of the same language that it really starts to change. With modern systems of communication there is little chance of losing contact, but in the field of medicine I am sure that the best way of sustaining the Anglo-American dialogue is for medical travelers to continue journeying both ways across the Atlantic.

---

1. Britons and Americans are growing words apart. The Times, June 28, 1978.
2. Anglophones of the future. The Times, June 28, 1978.
3. Medical staffing and prospects in the N.H.S. in England and Wales, 1977. Health Trends 1978; 10(3).

Reflections of an Honorary Medical Bureaucrat

FEBRUARY 22, 1979

Sir Derrick Dunlop was a charismatic figure in British medicine. He was highly regarded as a physician and teacher in Edinburgh and greatly respected as chairman of the Committee on Safety of Drugs. He also acquired a considerable reputation as an after-dinner speaker, always delighting his audiences with his wit.

During his long professional career Sir Derrick Dunlop has been general practitioner, consultant physician, professor of medicine and, recently, the first chairman of the Committee on Safety of Drugs, a role that he described as one of honorary medical bureaucrat. But he is also a brilliant raconteur, and when he spoke recently at a medical-society dinner, he delighted his audience as he reflected on the implications of the therapeutic revolution that has taken place during his professional lifetime.

Thus, Sir Derrick recalled that at the beginning of the present century the range of available drugs was small — indeed, he referred to a state of therapeutic nihilism and pointed out that even Osler's textbook devoted less than 10 per cent of the space to treatment. He could well remember such phrases as "arsenic might prove useful" and "general attention to health is important." But the labeling of the bottles was exquisite even though, in a paraphrase of Oliver Wendell Holmes, "If 80 per cent had been poured into the sea, only the fishes would have suffered." Of course, digitalis had been introduced more than a century earlier when Withering discovered the value of the foxglove in dropsy in 1776, but even so the days of bleedings, blisterings, sweatings and purgings were not far away; Sir Derrick thought that the younger physicians today, armed with what he called "the thunderbolts of Jove," might do well to recall the days when there were no antibiotics, no anticonvulsants, no vitamin B_{12} and no insulin.

The availability of such drugs has transformed the practice of medicine from the largely diagnostic art of Boerhaave and Laennec, based chiefly on a knowledge of anatomy, into a complex therapeutic science. Yet most of the discoveries have not been made as the result of a planned intellectual approach. Many drugs, like digitalis, were culled from the hedgerow, and quite a number of advances were due to sheer chance, whereby unexpected side effects of well known drugs were turned to good purpose. Thus, mercurial diuretics were introduced after it was noted that in syphilitic patients treated with mercury, a diuresis developed. Now, Sir Derrick pointed out, the commonest way of developing new drugs is by the method of minimal molecular alteration, or molecular roulette, as he called it.

But he cautioned that the limiting factor in the use of potent modern drugs is the problem of side effects and interaction. The old horse and buggy traveled slowly and caused few accidents; the modern automobile is fast and causes many. Similarly, the old bottle of medicine carried few risks, but there are many hazards with modern drugs, and nature seems to have become retaliatory and to be extracting a considerable degree of retribution. Nevertheless, Sir Derrick believed that if all drugs were prescribed with propriety there would be few risks. He considered the desire to take medicine the chief characteristic distinguishing man from the lower animals, and regretted that doctors seem to pander to the public's wants rather than to its needs. It takes time to obtain a history, to examine and to assess the patient, but only a moment to prescribe.

He thinks that the teaching of therapeutics leaves much to be desired. In British medical schools, pharmacology is often taught as a preclinical subject, the action of drugs being used to illustrate physiologic principles — a kind of acetylcholine type of clinical medicine. This method is fine for teaching physiology, but too often teaching about the therapeutic effect of drugs is inadequate and confined to the last few minutes of a session.

The persistent promotion of drugs by the pharmaceutical industry is often criticized, but nearly all new drugs in recent years have been introduced by the pharmaceutical industry, which carries out both fundamental and applied research and has been generous in its support of medical charities and foundations. But few industries have been subjected to more political criticism and control — even though, as Sir Derrick pointed out, in British hospitals the laundry bill is far larger than the pharmaceutical bill. He realized that the unpopularity of the pharmaceutical industry is related to its profit motive. But he could see nothing wicked in making a profit, even though he supposed that motivation without profit may eventually be seen in some Utopian society.

Meanwhile, he hoped that the independence of the pharmaceutical industry will be preserved so long as the ethical aspects of prescribing are kept under the strictest review and adequate trials are carried out before new drugs are released on an unsuspecting public all too ready to try the very next treatment that hits the headlines.

 PART TWO

The National Health Service

On Climbing Ladders

The effect of the National Health Service on the medical profession itself is a recurring theme throughout these extracts from the London Post. In particular, it will be noted that the divergence of interest between family doctors (general practitioners) and those practicing in hospitals has created many problems. General practitioners have often regarded themselves as second-class citizens and have resented the fact that students are taught, almost exclusively, by hospital-based doctors. Lord Moran, who was dean of St. Mary's Hospital Medical School for 25 years and Churchill's medical adviser throughout World War II, had no doubt that general practitioners and consultants were different. However, a remark that he made about people falling off ladders caused consternation. He said that the ladder to full consultant (staff) status in hospitals was steep and that many fell off it; how could people who fall off ladders be the same as those who do not?

The benefits conferred on the community as a whole as a result of the National Health Service have frequently been stressed. Sickness should no longer be the economic disaster it has sometimes been in the past, and no one is denied the best medical attention on account of lack of means. Old and young alike have reaped the benefit of this social change, and there is now a much greater uniformity of medical care throughout the country. But all social changes are apt to have their casualty lists, and the outstanding casualty in the National Health Service has been the medical profession itself.

Much has been said about the altered doctor-patient relation that has come about because the patient pays no fees directly to the doctor. Even more serious has been the division of the profession into groups within itself. This has occurred because of the organization of the National Health Service into two major parts: the hospital service on the one hand, and the general-practitioner service on the other. Unfortunately, the difference between the two groups has been exaggerated by the fact that doctors now rely on the Exchequer for their incomes, and in making claims for advances the relative merits of each group have naturally been stressed.

At the present time, the Royal Commission that was set up to inquire into the doctors' pay claim is listening to the evidence of all the interested parties, and the members have already heard the views of the British Medical Association, the Socialist Medical Association, the Royal College of Physicians and the Consultants' and Specialists' Committee. Because the evidence has been heard in public, it has been fully reported in the lay press, and the affairs of the profession fully exposed to the public eye, and any points of difference between different groups have tended to be overemphasized. Thus, whereas the Socialist Medical Association has stressed the advantages of a full-time salaried service, the other bodies giving evidence have claimed that the principle of part-time contracts in the health service is vital to preserve the doctor's sense of freedom and to allow the spirit of competition to continue.

It was, however, a chance remark that Lord Moran let slip concerning professional ladders that has caused the greatest consternation. While giving evidence in support of the merit award system, whereby a proportion of consultants are given as a reward for outstanding merit an annual bonus in addition to their salary, he was asked by the chairman whether he thought that general practitioners and consultants should be regarded as equals. He replied with an emphatic negative and said that in his twenty-five years as dean of St. Mary's Hospital Medical School, all the people of outstanding merit, with few exceptions, hoped to get on the hospital staff. But it was a ladder off which many fell, and how could people who fell off ladders be the same as those who did not? Although Lord Moran did his best to qualify his statement in letters to the *British Medical Journal* and to the *Lancet*, it triggered a flood of bitter correspondence in the medical journals and stimulated rather bewildered comment in the lay press.

It is, of course, true that the ladder to full hospital-staff appointments is steep, the climb is long, and many never reach the top. On the other hand there are many who never try to do so, and early in their careers they decide to enter the field of general practice, and in doing so they not infrequently follow in the tradition of their fathers and even grandfathers. There is a ladder, too, in this field, and although it may not be so steep, and although the man at the top may not be so conspicuous as the successful consultant, the view he gets from the top may be unrivaled when assessed in terms of the personal satisfaction derived from a job well done.

It is certainly unfortunate that in spite of many assertions that the general practitioner is the backbone of the profession, there has been a constant lowering of his status in the mind of the general public, with a corresponding inflation of the status of consultants. This is partly because the rapid advances in medicine have made specialization inevitable and partly because the National Health Service has overstressed the hospital side of the Service, with its highly trained consultants and specialists. The fact that for the most part their training is in a narrow field is often overlooked in comparisons of their ability and stature with those of general practitioners, who must be proficient over a much wider field, and many correspondents have pointed out that deprived of their hospital facilities and the backing of their teams, many consultants are lost.

Indeed, it might be an opportune moment to reflect upon the evolution of the hospital consultant. In days gone by, a period in general practice often constituted one of the most important steps on the ladder to a hospital-staff appointment, and there was certainly no suggestion that any man who entered general practice had fallen off any ladder. In fact, one correspondent in the present controversy has recalled how Harvey Cushing gave it as his opinion that no man should be allowed to become a specialist until he had first done ten years in general practice. Such names as Withering, Jenner and Mackenzie should be sufficient reminder that general practice may be a firm step on the ladder to success and fame.

When one is reflecting on such a theme as this, it is always worth turning to see what Sir William Osler would have said about it, and somewhere in his writing the answer is usually to be found. In this particular connection it is his essay on an Alabama student that fits the context best. Speaking to the Johns Hopkins Historical Club in 1895 he related the story of one Dr. John Bassett (1805–1851), of Huntsville, Alabama, whose name is not written on the scroll of fame, but who heard the call and forsook all and followed his ideal. After practicing in a country district for a few years he longed to visit the great centers of learning, and with his meager savings he made the journey to Europe in 1836. Having visited Edinburgh, Glasgow, Dublin and London, he crossed over to Paris, where he obtained an appointment as extern in Hôpital de la Charité under the surgeon Velpeau. His duties required him to be at the hospital at 6 o'clock, where he had to follow the surgeon, attend to his prescriptions and dress the patients. For this service he received no pay, but he wrote home that the work was of real benefit and that he had not been more gratified since being in Europe. He returned home after about a year's absence and apparently continued his practice in Huntsville until he died from pulmonary tuberculosis in 1851.

Osler pointed out that Dr. Bassett was a man of more than

ordinary gifts but that he was among the voiceless of the profession. Nevertheless, the majority of the great teachers, such as Velpeau, Andral and Broussais, whom he followed are now themselves but shadowy forms and almost as indistinct as the pupil. "To have striven, to have made an effort, to have been true to certain ideals, this alone is worth the struggle."

Dr. Bassett never fell from any ladder — indeed he climbed to the very top of his own. Osler found in one of Bassett's letters an itemized bill of twenty-eight extra charges that he incurred in traveling from London to Paris. Strangely enough, one of his items was for walking down a ladder — 1 shilling. He told this fellow to go to hell, and jumped over his ladder!

Medicine and Politics

Ever since the introduction of the National Health Service there have been recurring disputes between the medical profession and the politicians. These disputes have usually been about money. Indeed, Mr. Enoch Powell complained that money was the only subject that a Minister of Health was destined to discuss with the medical profession. Sometimes the dispute involves how much money the doctors should be paid, but at other times it is about the financial resources available for the treatment of patients and the maintenance of the NHS. In fact, it has been concern about these financial resources that has brought the profession into the sharpest conflict with the politicians.

The problem is that individual physicians are concerned that their individual patients should receive the best possible treatment, whereas the politicians are concerned that as many people as possible should benefit from the resources that the government is able to make available. Because it is so difficult to reconcile these two points of view, doctors and politicians are frequently in disagreement.

The remarkable article in the *Lancet* on September 24, 1966, by Professor Henry Miller would have attracted more attention initially if it had been entitled "Medicine and Politics" instead of appearing under the rather cryptic title of "Fifty Years after Flexner." For many must have imagined that they would be reading a heavy bacteriologic discourse on how in these fifty years, the bacteria had given way to increasing numbers of

78

elusive viral organisms as the commonest cause of all kinds of infections and other disease. But, fortunately, there are those who either read the *Lancet* from cover to cover or are aware that Abraham Flexner was born in Kentucky in 1866 to Jewish immigrants and that he was an educationalist and not to be confused with his brother, Simon, the bacteriologist. For no less than 99 (where was the hundredth?) eminent physicians, clinicians and teachers wrote to the *Lancet* endorsing the sentiments of the author and urging those in authority to act upon it. It was in fact this mass of impressive signatures that really underlined the significance of the article. Miller stressed the influence that the application of Flexner's ideas has had on American medicine. It was he who advocated the establishment of adequately staffed and adequately financed academic clinical units much on the lines of those in many European countries.

By contrast his ideas had been applied in Great Britain only slowly and halfheartedly, and Miller believes that most of the disappointments of Flexnerization in this country spring from the simple fact that money has never been made available to implement it. He claims that given adequate finance, most of the problems of the hospital service could be solved but that without it we are beating the air. He suggests that it is paradoxical that the two decades that have witnessed the greatest scientific advance in the history of medicine have also seen a decline in British hospital building unparalleled during the preceding century. Successive governments have been neglectful, and patients perhaps too tolerant, but he thinks that the medical profession is not free from blame. Cynical disillusion freely expressed at the hospital lunch table is rarely followed up by political pressure, and it has been left to figures on the fringe of medicine to inform and agitate public opinion about the appalling implications of present neglect. Unfortunately, election as president of a college or vice-chancellor of a university or to other positions of authority usually spells an inevitable preoccupation with the politically practical and insidious identification with central authority and a change of role from informed critic to uncomfortable apologist.

Apart from the inadequacy of the hospital-building program, Professor Miller also criticized the unrealistic approach to the staffing problems in hospitals, postgraduate training programs and the parsimonious attitude to research that has been partly responsible for the medical brain drain to countries with better facilities.

He believes, however, that the financial problems of medicine in this society will be overcome, and suggests that apart from an eccentric fringe the profession and the public are committed to the splendid conception of a comprehensive public medical service. He believes that it is a misconception that private practice can make any serious contribution to the provisions of modern medical care, and thinks that when we say we cannot afford properly equipped universities or hospitals, we are really saying that we prefer to spend our money in other ways. He admitted that to speak of the impending disintegration of the hospital service is to invite the accusation of alarmism, but there are some serious omens that clearly point in this direction. He said that the expansion, development and revitalization of British medicine that is urgently needed will be an exacting and exhausting exercise for everybody engaged in it:

. . . and if after due consideration of priorities the nation is unwilling to provide the necessary resources, there will be many who will return with clear consciences to the comfortable cultivation of their professional gardens. After all the practice of medicine is still a fascinating pursuit even in a declining civilization.

Mr. Enoch Powell's new book, which is entitled *Medicine and Politics*,[1] is an equally remarkable piece of literature — and it is interesting to compare and contrast the approach of the politician with that of the clinical professor.

Mr. Powell, who was the minister of health for three years and three months, admits that the unnerving discovery that every minister of health makes at or near the outset of his term of office is that the only subject that he is destined ever to discuss with the medical profession is money. He believes that this is because nationalization has made money the sole terminology of intercourse between profession and government. All discontents and inadequacies can be externalized and rationalized by a single anthropomorphic explanation, and it is the fault of a miserly minister or treasury or cabinet.

Thus, every need is politicized in a financial form, and "Give us more money" becomes the refrain of the profession. Furthermore, the universal exchequer financing of the service endows everyone providing it with a vested interest in denigrating it, so that it presents the unique spectacle of an undertaking that is run down by everyone engaged in it.

He admits that it is because medical care under the National Health Service is rendered free to the consumer at the point of consumption that supply and demand are not kept in balance by price. Indeed, the demand, for all practical purposes, is unlimited, and with every new development in treatment it tends to increase. On the other hand the supply is limited by governmental action through the parliamentary votes for the National Health Service and in the hospital service, the Minister of Health then decides how much each hospital board shall be allowed to spend each year. There is thus in effect a rationing system of medical care determined by political expediency. On the other hand Mr. Powell points out that the public is encouraged to believe that rationing in medical care was banished by the National Health Service and that the very idea of applying rationing to medical care is immoral and repugnant. Nevertheless, waiting times for clinic appointments and waiting lists for admission are obvious manifestations of a rationing system. But, again, Powell points out that the necessity for these covert forms of rationing springs from "Parkinson's law of hospital beds," which asserts that the number of patients always tends to equality with the number of beds available for them to lie in and he admits that even given the insight and the will to do so, the politicians could not alter this law.

Turning to the differing points of view of the politician and the doctor Mr. Powell recognizes that by tradition and training, the doctor upholds the independence of individual professional judgment and accepts responsibility for each patient, whereas the politician is concerned with the general consequences of individual decisions. Furthermore, he points out that in all governments the decisions of policy must be taken by the layman.

There is no doubt that Powell himself does not believe that apparently free medical attention at the time of need is the right method of providing a national health service. Indeed, he concludes that a change in the relation of medicine and politics will only be heralded when the number of family doctors and the volume of consultation and hospital treatment tendered outside the National Health Service shows a marked and continuing rise (and it will be noted that this is quite the reverse of Professor Miller's view).

Nevertheless, the tragedy of Mr. Powell's critical appraisal of the present situation is that although clearly an expert diagnostician, he can offer no treatment, admitting in his final sentence that he has pursued an argument in a circle — "the circle in which Medicine and Politics are imprisoned in the National Health Service."

Expressed in other words the tragedy seems to be that the doctors and the politicians are running on parallel lines that will never meet, but if they do not, the patients will eventually be the losers.

---

1.   Powell JE. Medicine and politics. London: Pitman Medical Publishing, 1966.

Elephants Galore

The administration of the National Health Service has never been entirely satisfactory. The tripartite administrative structure — with the family-practitioner service, the hospital service, and the public-health service all being separately administered — was criticized from the start. There was considerable debate about possible ways of integrating the service within a single administrative framework, and some of the initial proposals are considered in this Post.

The Green Papers mentioned are discussion papers published by the government before the introduction of legislation that may be controversial, in order to test public opinion. The absorption of the Ministry of Health within a large, new Department of Health and Social Security (DHSS), headed by a Secretary of State responsible for the whole field of health and social security, was not popular with the doctors. Mr. Kenneth Robinson, the last Minister of Health, had been well liked by the medical profession, and the NHS had prospered under his care. Mr. Richard Crossman, with much wider responsibilities as Secretary of State at the DHSS, was seen as rather a remote figure residing at the Elephant and Castle.

Between Guy's Hospital, near London Bridge, and Camberwell Green, there was for many years a famous tavern called the Elephant & Castle — always known affectionately as the Elephant; the road junction where it stood and indeed the underground station at the southern end of the Bakerloo Line were known by the same name. Alas! the Elephant was bombed during the war, and when in their wisdom the civil servants and their political masters decided that many governmental departments must migrate away from Whitehall, a tall building with glass sides arose near the site of the bombed Elephant, and there the Ministry of Health established itself and thereafter the Elephant has been in the minds of the doctors, not the source of a pint of ale, but the seat of the Minister who in some way seems to wield remote control over their destinies and the source of an ever-increasing volume of memoranda and reports on the administration of the National Health Service. Of course, the administrative structure of the National Health Service has never been satisfactory, the chief criticism being that the family-doctor service, the hospital service and the public-health service have all been separately administered.

For many years the medical profession has been advocating the unification of these three aspects of medical care within a single administrative structure, and some years ago a committee of the British Medical Association under the chairmanship of Sir Arthur Porritt suggested that such a unification could be attained if a number of area health boards were set up. This phrase was used in the Green Paper[1] published in 1968 by Mr. Kenneth Robinson when he was Minister of Health, but it seemed likely that the boards as he proposed them would have come under the control of corresponding areas of local government — an occurrence that the medical profession thought most undesirable.

Subsequently, the Ministry of Health lost its identity in the newly formed Department of Health and Social Security, and Mr. Robinson was displaced in favor of Mr. Richard Crossman, who is now the Secretary of State in this vast department at the Elephant and Castle. In his turn he has prepared a second Green Paper[2] on the future structure of the National Health Service, which has now been presented to Parliament and released for discussion by all interested parties. His proposals differ from those of Mr. Robinson in conceding that there would be disadvantages in placing area health boards under local-authority control, although the Royal Commission on Local Government[3] had been in favor of doing so.

Mr. Crossman has substituted the term "area health authority" for area health board, and he proposes to establish 90 such authorities covering areas geographically the same as those to be covered by the enlarged local authorities proposed by the Royal Commission. He also recommends that these local authorities take over much of the social and welfare work previously administered by the Medical Officer of Health.

Mr. Crossman proposes that the area health authorities consist of 20 to 25 members, of whom one third shall be appointed by the professions working in the service, one third by the local authority and one third, including the chairman, by the Secretary of State. The area health authorities will administer the existing hospital and specialist services, the family-doctor service and certain services such as ambulances, community health, family planning, maternity services and the school health service, all of which are now provided by local health authorities.

The population served by each area authority will vary from 200,000 to 1,300,000; to ensure local participation in running the health services, it is proposed that district committees be established in relation to the areas served by district hospitals. Half the membership of these committees would be drawn from the appropriate health authority, and the other half from people living or working in the district. It is thought that these committees would be used by the area health authorities to supervise the running of the services at the district level, serving as channels through which local people could keep the area authority informed of local problems and ensuring that the authority was exposed to the full vigor of local opinion in the professions and of local users of the health service. On the other hand, Mr. Crossman emphasized the point that these district committees would have no statutory powers and no separate budgets. He also stressed the fact that although the Secretary of State will allocate funds to the new area health authorities, he must be satisfied that the money is spent to the best advantage.

The central department of health will therefore need to concern itself more closely than in the past with expenditure and efficiency at the local level, applicable both to the standards of provision to be aimed at and to the priorities to be adopted between competing demands. To ensure this, Mr. Crossman states that the full range of powers of guidance — and, if necessary, direction — required for this purpose will be available to the Secretary of State. To co-ordinate overall planning of the health services, it is also proposed that a number of regional health councils be established. They would be constructed by grouping the areas of several health authorities, probably between three and nine. The membership of these councils would reflect that of the area health authorities and would include a representative from each area health authority in the region and several members appointed by the professions and the universities. One of the most important functions of these councils would be planning the regional hospital and specialist services, and they would carry special responsibility for organizing postgraduate medical education. They might also sponsor research into the clinical and operational problems of the health services throughout the region. In most of these activities the role of the councils would be advisory, but in view of their membership, their advice would carry great weight.

Mr. Crossman points out that the National Health Service is now one of the country's largest industries — employing 750,000 people with an estimated budget of £1,500,000,000 for 1970–1971. He believes that the proposals in the Green Paper will integrate the existing services and at the same time provide the necessary flexibility for each local area to respond to the changing needs of the community in the coming decades. Apart from the proposed administrative structure and its relation to local authorities the Green Paper is open for discussion, and much comment has already been forthcoming. *The Times* and the *British Medical Journal* both see the way opened for a broad extension of central direction and control. In a leading article entitled "Doctor's Dilemma" *The Times*[4] has seized upon Mr. Crossman's statement that the central department will need to concern itself more closely with the expenditure and efficiency of the administration at the local level and that the Secretary of State will have the full range of powers of guidance and, if necessary, direction. The leader writer believes that such a process of centralization would be undesirable for a number of reasons. Certain facilities are so specialized and expensive that they can only be planned nationally, but it is feared that in other matters, there is the danger that there will be central intervention on points that would be much better left to local or regional discretion. Doctors might well find themselves frustrated by decisions taken by those beyond their reach. *The Times* believes, however, that the doctors are partly to blame for this because of their total rejection of the idea of the Health Service under local governmental control, and wonders whether they realize that their rejection of such a control could well result in the far tighter central control that seems likely from the Green Paper proposals.

The *British Medical Journal*[5] regrets that Mr. Crossman did not propose the establishment of district committees based on one or more district hospitals as the main peripheral administrative authorities for integrating the health services, and hopes that there may still be time for second thoughts on this matter. Like *The Times*, the *British Medical Journal* sees the whole picture as one of increased central control with strengthened regional offices of the health department — smaller elephants on the periphery. The *British Medical Journal* also notes that in spite of the firm statement that the Health Service will not be administered by local governments, the proposed area health authorities coincide with those of the new local governmental areas, so that the stage is set for a merger at any time in the future.

After an interval for discussion of the Green Paper the Government will publish a White Paper with definite proposals that will receive the assent of Parliament, and so the reconstruction of the National Health Service will be set actively in motion. The *British Medical Journal* urges the doctors to study the proposals and to be ready to offer informed comment. Unfortunately, however, the busy doctor has little time to read and digest the tremendous volume of official documents that are being thrust upon him and that may alter his whole professional environment. Decisions are often reported by the Ministry to have been taken after "consultation with representatives of the profession," but unfortunately the basis of these consultations is often uncertain, and many consider their representation unrepresentative.

For many middle-aged doctors there is a feeling that the rules are being changed halfway through the game. The suggested administrative rearrangements will mean the termination of existing contracts and the negotiation of new ones with different employing authorities, and it is feared that pension rights may also change.

This all seems a long way from the care of the patient, and it will be sad if his interests should become lost in the complexities of an administrative structure of big elephants, middling-sized elephants and baby elephants. At present there seems to be a real danger that this could happen. Fortunately, however, the practicing physician, when first becoming obsessed with the fear of being trapped in the administrator's net, can still escape to the world of reality through the contacts he makes with his patients. And just as I despaired of having a light-hearted note on which to conclude this "green" Post, I received a letter from a grateful patient suffering from hemochromatosis whom I had referred some time ago to the unit most interested and competent in handling this problem. He was writing to tell me of his latest attendance for reassessment, when he had been seen by a new, dour Scottish registrar (resident). "He asked me about my alcohol intake," wrote my patient, "and I told him I like a couple of gins before dinner and a couple of glasses of wine with my meal. The Scottish registrar looked at me so straight and so seriously that I asked him if that would do my liver any harm. 'Man,' he replied, 'it's no your liver I'm worrying aboot — it's your pocket!'" That letter kept me chuckling to myself all day, and the elephants were all forgotten — at any rate for that day.

1. Great Britain, Ministry of Health. National Health Service: The administrative structure of the medical and related services in England and Wales. London: Her Majesty's Stationery Office, 1968.
2. Great Britain, Department of Health and Social Security. The future structure of the National Health Service. London: Her Majesty's Stationery Office, 1968.
3. Great Britain, Ministry of Health. Reform of local government in England. London: Her Majesty's Stationery Office, 1970.
4. Leading Article. Doctors' dilemma. The Times, February 12, 1970, p 11.
5. Leading Article. New green paper. Br Med J 1970; 1:379-380.

Effectiveness and Efficiency in Health Care

JULY 27, 1972

Dr. Cochrane's monograph on effectiveness and efficiency in health care has been widely accepted as an outstanding contribution to the debate about the importance of making the best use of available resources. A protagonist of the randomized controlled trial, he recognized that his proposals were both provocative and controversial.

There have been few objective appraisals of the National Health Service, partly because of the political emotions that are aroused when there is any suggestion that it may have any serious imperfection and partly because of the medical emotions that are aroused when there is any suggestion that its improvement might require an alteration of the attitude of the medical profession. In his Rock Carling monograph[1] just published by the Nuffield Provincial Hospitals Trust, Dr. A. L. Cochrane, director of the Medical Research Council Epidemiology Unit at Cardiff, had no inhibitions in his random reflections on the effectiveness and efficiency of the health services. He recalls that when he was a medical student in the 1930's, there was a rally in a London suburb in support of the idea of a health service, and he carried a banner proclaiming that "all effective treatment must be free." The slogan was a flop, and he doubted whether he could then have defined the word "effective," but largely as a result of the social injustices of the 1930's, he remained emotionally biased in favor of a national health service. As a result of traveling widely he has concluded that the present British Service is probably the best of a very poor lot, but now views it as one would a favorite child showing marked delinquent tendencies.

The Service was introduced at a time when there was a great advance in therapeutic possibilities. Until the end of the 19th century, environmental factors alone were important in improving morbidity and mortality statistics, the available medical therapy being largely ineffective. On the other hand the layman has always had an uncritical belief in the ability of the medical profession at least to help if not to cure, and Osler noted that "a desire to take medicine is perhaps the great feature which distinguishes man from other animals." This led to the belief that for every symptom there must be a pill, an operation or some other therapy that would at least help. The gradual appearance of effective remedies enhanced the status of the doctor, but the extent of prescribing was controlled by economic factors until they were removed by the National Health Service, which Dr. Cochrane sees as a national organization giving a blank check both to the demands of patients and to the wishes of doctors. Most industrial organizations of comparable size would have had a research section checking on the effectiveness of the service that they were providing, but for the first 15 years of its life, no such research was carried out in the National Health Service. In evaluating the evidence for effectiveness and efficiency, Dr. Cochrane points out that account must be taken of both opinion and the results of experiments. In recent years, he believes, the former has been upgraded, and the latter downgraded. The upgrading of opinion has many causes, but the television interviewer is one of the most important. He wants everything brief, dramatic and black and white, but he seldom asks for evidence for statements. In medicine, clinical opinion is the commonest form of evidence offered. Death is the best index of success or failure since other indexes are more difficult to evaluate. Observational evidence is better than opinion, but carefully planned experiment should form the basis of all reliable evidence.

Dr. Cochrane believes that much of the credit for introducing the experimental approach into clinical medicine belongs to Sir Austin Bradford Hill; he suggests that there should be a Bradford award for the author of the best medical statistical paper of the year. The randomized control trial makes it possible to test the hypothesis that one treatment is better than another and to express the results in the form of the probability whether or not the differences found are due to chance. The double-blind randomized trial eliminates the possibility of a great deal of bias. Ethical considerations may limit the scope of trials; subjective observations still cannot be assessed, and the assessment of the quality of life remains difficult. Nevertheless, Dr. Cochrane believes that the problem of evaluation is the first priority of the National Health Service, and for this purpose the randomized control trial is the most suitable instrument in spite of its snags.

Dr. Cochrane considers it important to evaluate the effectiveness and efficiency of methods of preventive medicine, treatment and diagnosis. Much has been achieved in the field of preventive medicine, but the value of each exercise is not always assessed. There seems no doubt about the value of such programs as immunization against diphtheria and BCG vaccination. On the other hand, the value of cervical-smear tests in the prevention of carcinoma of the cervix is less certain. No randomized control trial has ever been carried out to determine its value, and the death rate from carcinoma of the cervix was falling when the smear test was introduced and has continued to do so in most areas at about the same rate. Journalists and television interviewers did not distinguish themselves when the subject was under discussion, and never had there been less appeal to evidence and more to opinion.

On the subject of smoking, he said that the evidence against the cigarette was overwhelming, but before encouraging everyone to give up smoking cigarettes, he thought we should be well advised to control our population increase since overpopulation could be described as the country's greatest problem, although it is difficult to persuade people of that fact.

In therapy the most important type of inefficiency is really a combination of two separate groups, the use of ineffective therapies and the use of effective therapies at the wrong times. Thus, although the effect of placebos has been shown by randomized control trial to be significant, and their use in the correct place is to be encouraged, the use of relatively expensive drugs as placebos is inefficient, and the amount of inefficient prescribing is known to be very large and expensive.

The incorrect place of treatment is another form of inefficiency (possibly the least recognized type of inefficiency), but it seems probable that the increasing cost of hospitalization will force attention to it. Traditions have grown up concerning the correct place for treating particular diseases, and until recently no one has regarded these traditional decisions as hypotheses that should be tested. Thus, many physicians have held bed rest and supervision in the hospital to be the best treatment for myocardial infarction, but the results of a trial in Bristol,[2] in which hospital treatment (including a variable time in a coronary-care unit) was compared with treatment at home, do not suggest that there is any medical gain in admission to a hospital, as compared with treatment at home, for cases of acute ischemic heart disease. Similarly, an abnormally long stay in the hospital may reflect inefficiency. The average length of hospital stay in this country is greater than in some other countries — presumably owing to the economic facts of the National Health Service; large differences in length of stay for the same condition in different parts of the country and between different consultants have been noted. Thus, no harmful effects have been noted in patients discharged shortly after hernia repair, and patients with varicose veins who were treated as outpatients seemed to do as well as those detained in the hospital.

The chronic outpatient is another problem. Dr. Cochrane mentions a number of reasons why some patients continue attending an outpatient clinic. Some with chronic diseases did so before the National Health Service to avoid paying their doctors, and continue to do so now; others seem to have a wish for continuous surveillance that their own doctor has not time to offer. Still others are asked to attend for research purposes or because the consultant in charge of the clinic is apparently anxious to build his empire. Diabetic clinics, with large numbers of persons with maturity-onset diabetes, contain a high proportion of chronic outpatients. Dr. Cochrane suggests that this is a wasteful use of hospital resources and is only contributing to the state of medical inflation that he regards as almost analogous to the industrial inflation that threatens to undermine the economy. The external factors mainly responsible are the pharmaceutical industry, the mass media, medical research and the lack of applied research. More planned applied operational research using scientific technics generally acceptable to the profession would help to evaluate the present methods of prevention, treatment, and diagnosis of disease, and more effective methods might emerge. Dr. Cochrane believes, however, that if the efficiency and effectiveness of the National Health Service is to be improved as the result of such research, there may have to be changes that will decrease the clinical freedom of doctors. Indications for prescriptions, diagnostic tests, admission and length of stay in hospital would become more clearly defined, and doctors might have to justify variations from these norms. There might also be limitations on administrative freedom, so that requests for additional facilities would have to be supported with hard evidence of cost and the gain to be expected for the patient.

There would also be a shift in emphasis from hospital care to community care. Admission to a hospital would take place only after full outpatient investigation and when some intensive form of therapy was required. The district hospital might well become smaller, with the local community fulfilling the need of patients requiring nursing care that they cannot receive in their own homes, and with well trained general practitioners working from community health centers.

These are clearly controversial issues, and Dr. Cochrane recognizes that his suggestions are provocative. Nevertheless, he believes that his investigation into the working of the clinical sections of the National Health Service suggests that this sector is subject to a severe inflation with output rising much less than would be expected from the input. He believes that the inflation could be controlled by science, in particular by the wide use of randomized control trials. But in an apologetic postscript he fears that he has perhaps been too critical of his clinical colleagues, for whom he admits the greatest admiration and affection. He had been comparing them with an absolute standard — and yet what other profession encourages publications about its errors and carries out investigations into the effects of its actions? What judge or headmaster has encouraged randomized control trials in their "therapeutic" and "deterrent" actions? In many respects Dr. Cochrane considers the medical profession far ahead of other professions in self-criticism.

These are soothing sentiments for any who may have resented his apparently cold, impersonal experimental approach to the evaluation of the clinical method. I wonder, however, what his opinion would be of a conversation that I recently had with an elderly chronic outpatient in a diabetic clinic. Her tolbutamide had been withdrawn on her previous visit, and her urine remained sugar free and her blood sugar satisfactory on her restricted-carbohydrate diet. In reply to a query about any other drugs she was taking she pushed a piece of paper across the desk, on which was written — digitalis, furosemide (Lasix), potassium and carbimazole (Neo-Mercazole). Without being asked, she then gave a catalogue of her various symptoms and past medical history. She explained that she had suffered from headaches ever since she had a swelling removed from the top of her head many years ago, that she was breathless and had swollen ankles and had awful abdominal pain. She was sure that all the trouble came from her thyroid gland, which had been too active for years, but which she was sure was now going the other way. When she paused for breath I asked if she had seen her family doctor — to which she immediately replied that he had no time to listen and when she had last seen him she had told him about her awful abdominal pain but he had simply said, "Good afternoon" and prescribed more tablets. And so she had walked down the village to the public library (what else could she do?), though she could not walk fast because of her sciatica, but when she looked it up in the book in the public library, she was sure that her thyroid gland *was* going the other way; she had "the myxedema" — the only thing was that her face was pink instead of pale and she did not feel very cold, but apart from that everything was right for the myxedema. "And thank you for listening doctor — but could you please examine my abdomen because I still have the awful abdominal pain!" She did not appear to be in pain, nor did her rapid flow of speech suggest she had myxedema. I regret to say that I also said, "Good afternoon Mrs. X," and gave her another appointment for our chronic-diabetic outpatient clinic.

Dr. Cochrane would probably frown, but where would she fit into a randomized control trial? Our consultation would not register much output compared with input, but we had perhaps dispensed a little humanity by listening to the old lady who had had to go to the public library to seek information her own family doctor had not had the time to give.

1. Cochrane AL. Effectiveness and efficiency (The Rock Carling Fellowship, 1971). London: Oxford University Press, for the Nuffield Provincial Hospitals Trust, 1972.
2. Mather HG, Pearson NG, Read KLQ, et al. Acute myocardial infarction: home and hospital treatment. Br Med J 1971; 3:334-338.

Reorganization 1974 — for Better or for Worse?

MARCH 29, 1973

The consultations about the proposed reorganization of the National Health Service were protracted. Many practicing physicians felt overwhelmed by the apparent complexities of the proposals and were reluctant to accept managerial responsibilities. A few enthusiasts urged the professionals and particularly the physicians to involve themselves in these matters, lest the lay administrators usurp the traditional role of the physician as a leader in medical administrative affairs.

Later this year, the National Health Service will celebrate its silver jubilee, and next year it is due to undergo a complete reorganization. Ever since the Service began there have been problems arising from its tripartite structure. Thus, the work of general practitioners has been organized by a network of executive councils, the work in district hospitals has been organized by regional hospital boards, and that in teaching hospitals by boards of governors, with local authorities retaining responsibility for the community health services. For many years it has been suggested by many different people that an integrated service with one authority for all three aspects of health care would be more efficient. Consultations on the broad form of such an integrated service have been taking place between representatives of the health professions and the Department of Health for a considerable time, and interim reports have appeared, but the bill to permit the changes to be put into effect in April 1974 is now passing through Parliament. Most doctors have been too busy with their professional commitments to follow these developments closely, but they have been warned repeatedly by the British Medical Association to do so because of the radical nature of many of the changes proposed. These changes have been summarized in a document recently published by the Department of Health and Social Security and described as the Grey Book[1] — because of the color of its cover.

This book is certainly not to be regarded as suitable bedside reading for anyone allergic to modern management technic, which is what it is all about, and, indeed, it is written in the jargon of that discipline and illustrated with complicated flow charts, exhibits and job descriptions, due acknowledgment being given to McKinsey and Company, Incorporated, and to the Health Service Organization Research Unit of Brunel University. More regard seems to have been paid to doctrinaire principles of management than to the practical problems of treating the sick. Certainly, the first chapter opens with the statement that the objective in reorganizing the National Health Service is to make it possible for health care to be improved. It is also stated that this objective depends primarily on the people in the health-care professions, with management playing only a subsidiary part. Nevertheless, thereafter the emphasis is almost entirely on the management arrangements in the "new" National Health Service.

First the framework is described. There will be Area Health Authorities (AHA), including some Area Health Authorities (Teaching) (AHA[T]) with particular medical and dental teaching responsibilities, accountable to Regional Health Authorities (RHA), which are in turn to be responsible to the Secretary of State at the Department of Health and Social Security (DHSS) for the effectiveness and efficiency of the service provided. The AHA's will be coterminous geographically with local authority areas, and each AHA will be required to set up a Family Practitioner Committee (FPC) to administer the contracts of family doctors. The areas will be divided into districts with a population of about 250,000. Each district will have a district general hospital (DGH), and there will be a District Management Team (DMT) to manage each district. Medical membership of such a team will be restricted to one elected hospital consultant, one elected family physician and the District Community Physician (DCP), who in many cases will be the doctor who was previously medical officer of health. Regional Medical Officers (RMO) and Area Medical Officers (AMO) will also be appointed to advise the Regional and Area Authorities, which will be composed of small groups of laymen with a few representatives of the health professions — medical, dental, nursing and other professions ancillary to medicine. They will be appointed by the Secretary of State, not elected by any interested party, and it has been stated that they will be chosen for their managerial capabilities. Policy will be determined by the Department of Health, with certain responsibility delegated to the Regional and Area Authorities, which in turn will delegate responsibility to District Management Teams. Much stress has been laid on the fact that this delegation of responsibility downward will be matched by a concept that there will be accountability upward!

Day-to-day executive action will be taken by the "officers" of the various authorities, the chief executive officer at each level being described as the administrator, with a treasurer responsible for financial affairs and a nursing officer for the nursing services.

Professional advisory committees are to be established for the RHA's and AHA's and will be consulted before important planning and allocation decisions are made. There is considerable apprehension in the profession, however, that these committees may well be much less democratic than the various medical advisory committees that evolved during the earlier years of the National Health Service. It is even suspected that this may be one of the aims of the proposed plans. Thus, although it is acknowledged that the first duty of a clinician is to practice clinical medicine and exercise clinical autonomy and so be his own manager, it is stressed that in so doing, every doctor makes demands on resources that have to be reconciled with one another. Furthermore, his clinical actions interact in complex ways with the work of others in both the health and the personal social services. It is also acknowledged that clinicians are important innovators and that their ideas must be picked up by management, on which they unavoidably have an impact. It is suggested that the benefits of this impact will be greatest and the ill-effects least if clinicians take an active part in management and carry out their clinical duties with an understanding of the effects on other parts of the service. They should also accept the need to be committed to proposed changes and developments.

There is concern, too, that the customers will have less opportunity for making their views known than in the past. Hitherto, the Regional Hospital Board and Hospital Management Committees have been largely composed of members of the public, many with long experience of hospital affairs, many (though, of course, not all) sympathetic to the efforts of the doctors, and all acting as keen watchdogs of the patients' welfare. As already mentioned, these bodies are to be replaced by the small appointed Regional and Area Health Authorities, with the views of the public represented through Community Health Councils (CHC), which will be able to visit hospitals but will have only advisory functions. The public is being given additional protection by the appointment of an ombudsman to whom complaints may be addressed, so long as they do not relate to matters of clinical judgment, which can still be challenged through existing channels.

Although not disputing the advantages of integrating the three parts of the National Health Service, the British Medical Association has been fully alert to the risks to the medical profession in the proposed changes and has been active in protecting their interests. In a recent leading article,[2] the *British Medical Journal* reported the present situation and in the same issue published a letter[3] from the Secretary of the British Medical Association to the profession, emphasizing the points on which assurances have been sought from the Department of Health.

Most important is the preservation of clinical freedom, which seems to be ensured by the statement in the Grey Book that the role of the specialist in community medicine will not involve managerial authority over doctors giving personal clinical services, but the Council of the British Medical Association believes that the principle of clinical freedom is so important that it should be embodied in the Act of Parliament. Similarly, the importance of strong medical advisory machinery has been stressed by the Council, and it is hoped that a statutory obligation will be placed on the health authorities to consult the recognized medical advisory committee. Continued vigilance is promised as the bill proceeds through all its stages. But it is not only the members of the medical profession who are skeptical of the great emphasis on management in the proposed upheaval of the National Health Service. The *Financial Times*,[4] although it believes that Sir Keith Joseph is probably the best British Health Minister since Aneurin Bevan, who introduced the National Health Service in 1948, suggested that he could learn something from a recent utterance of the Socialist leader, Mr. Harold Wilson. It was ironical that Mr. Wilson had spoken of exalting the role of the individual and encouraging him or her to make personal choices at a time when a Conservative Government had just introduced the greatest web of controls over our daily lives yet devised in peacetime. But never mind — it was the idea that was important; the criticism leveled by the *Financial Times* at the Grey Book, of wonderment for future historians, was that nowhere does it come to grips with the needs of the patient as an individual. The prose is criticized as being so turgid and complicated that to get from one page to another, it is necessary to have a night's rest in between, and the writer claimed that he had stopped because he repeatedly met the initials "AHA" as if this were an exclamation of exultation at some revelation. But it never was. The mass of organizational charts looked like London Underground maps without the simplifying advantages of the Circle Line, and none of the charts had a "Way in" sign for the ordinary person — and, worse, no "Way out." The whole thing seemed to be a giant forcefed dose of management to be taken as often as the medical personnel and administrators who will themselves be trapped within those management mazes are programmed to make one take it. Indeed, the *Financial Times* believes that this reorganization is based on the thinking of a bygone decade, and although it is probably too late to scrap the whole project, it urges Sir Keith to modify the present bill as it passes through Parliament — and at least to ensure that there are representatives of patients throughout the new administrative structure.

As a physician practicing within the National Health Service, I have always thought that the function of management is to provide the conditions in which the doctors and nurses can treat the patients. Admittedly, the profession must be prepared to give advice about what they require, and because medical and nursing resources are both restricted and expensive commodities, there has to be some central body to decide upon priorities, or more bluntly, as Mr. Enoch Powell[5] once said, to decide how medical care shall be rationed. This is the inescapable responsibility of the Department of Health, and the existing chains of medical advisory committees have provided the Department with adequate information to know what is required to bring the best available help to patients. Many doctors have already ceased attending medical committees because their advice so rarely seems to have been heeded. They have returned to tend their clinical gardens, where they have found greater satisfaction, and it is doubtful that many will be coaxed back to participate in this new managerial revolution. They just hope that it will not interfere too much with the way they wish to treat their patients, but if it does so they will doubtless take action to ensure that not only the rights of their patients but also the traditions of the medical profession are respected.

1. Great Britain, Department of Health and Social Security. Management arrangements for the reorganised National Health Service. London: Her Majesty's Stationery Office, 1972.

2. Leading Article. Progress report on N.H.S. reorganisation. Br Med J 1973; 1:252.

3. B.M.A. Letter to the profession: progress report. Br Med J 1973; 1:29s.

4. What Sir Keith can learn from Mr. Wilson. Financial Times, January 24, 1973.

5. Powell JE. A new look at medicine and politics. London: Pitman Medical Publishing Company, 1972:38.

April 1, 1974 —
Before and After

The date April 1, 1974, was an important one for the National Health Service, in that the first major reorganization of the Service took place. The tripartite administrative structure was brought to an end, and the hospital service, the general-practitioner service, and the public-health service were all brought within a single administration. The country remained divided into Regions as before, with 14 Regional Health Authorities. Within each of these authorities there was set up a number of Area Health Authorities — 90 throughout the country — and each Area authority comprised one or more Districts. The introduction of the Area created a new, intermediate tier of management, and although the principle of delegating responsibility downward was intended to facilitate decision making, the parallel principle of requiring accountability to be projected upward greatly impaired it.

As I was driving to the hospital on April 1, I was interested to learn from my radio that April Fool's Day came to be so named because of a medieval practice of allowing insane persons to be abroad on that day. On arriving at the hospital, I was therefore much relieved to see no evidence of any disturbed persons and no sign of any outward change, although the Management Committee and the Regional Hospital Board had disappeared overnight and had been replaced by an Area Health Authority and a Regional Health Authority in the quiet coup that finally marked the end of the old National Health Service and the beginning of the reorganized Service.[1] But the *British Medical Journal*[2] had already warned that there would be no fanfares for April 1 — the day would come and go quietly, with the doctors and nurses carrying on much as before and the public largely unaware that a massive administrative reform of a multi-million-pound state organization had taken place after several years of political argument. Nevertheless, the date April 1, 1974, will long be remembered as a watershed in the affairs of the Service, and it is an opportunity to review the achievement of the Service so far and to try and assess its future prospects. It is right to recall that the introduction of the Service whereby medical and surgical care was made universally available without cost at the time of need (apart from small prescription charges and token charges for certain appliances) was recognized as an act of social justice that received the general approval of both the politicians and the electorate, no matter what their political allegiance.

The main problems of the Service have been due to the lack of adequate funds in the face of ever-increasing costs, the initial budget of £400 million in 1948 having risen to approximately £3,000 million at present. Recurrent economic crises have been the cause of the postponement of many capital projects, and many groups of workers in the Service have been inadequately paid. The original tripartite administrative structure, whereby the hospitals, the family-doctor service and the community health services were separately administered, had obvious disadvantages; one of the main objectives of the present reorganization was to replace this tripartite structure with a single authority, although at regional, area and district levels. It is to be hoped that this unification, which was, in fact, advocated by the medical profession, will eventually bring benefit to the patients, but there is still considerable apprehension about the great emphasis on management in the new Service. This management will be mainly in the hands of small teams of administrators and Regional and Area Authorities composed of small numbers of persons selected for their managerial ability, in place of the more democratically nominated members of the hospital boards and management committees who gave loyal service and advice in the original National Health Service. There is minimal medical representation on Regional and Area Health Authorities and on District Management Teams, but it has been agreed that medical advice will be sought through medical advisory machinery.

Ever since the Service began, both the medical and indeed the nursing professions have been subject to many strains and stresses. In the early days the general practitioners were poorly paid, but they retained their status as independent contractors, and as the result of forceful negotiation they have now achieved satisfactory terms and conditions of service from the Department of Health; by present standards they are adequately paid. On the other hand, the hospital consultants and specialists, who have always been salaried, either on a whole-time or a part-time basis, have seen their relative position deteriorate, in terms of both workload and salary. Thus, the *British Medical Journal*[3] points out that during the past 10 years, the salaries of hospital consultants have risen by only 71 per cent, whereas those of the junior staff have risen by 150 per cent and the income of the general practitioners by 108 per cent. Furthermore, the workload of the consultants has steadily increased because of the greater demands on the hospital services, the poor recruitment in certain specialties and increasingly generous off-duty time for junior staff, whereas the consultants themselves are subject to an open-ended contract with no fixed hours of duty.

It is unfortunate that the introduction of the reorganized National Health Service should have coincided not only with such a period of discontent among the consultants but also with a period of unprecedented financial stringency and then with an unexpected change of government.

The new Secretary of State at the Department of Health and Social Security, Mrs. Barbara Castle, is doubtless fully aware of the problems confronting the reorganized health service. In fact, the Labour Party was not opposed to many of the principles involved in the reorganization, but in the debate on the Queen's Speech, Mrs. Castle criticized the lack of democratic involvement in the management of the new service and hoped that it would be possible to make the new Area Authorities into more representative bodies; she indicated her intention of increasing the power of the Community Health Councils, which are to be set up to protect the consumer interest. Mrs. Castle also referred to the attitude of the new government to prescription charges and private practice within the National Health Service hospitals. She promised that her Party's pledge to abolish prescription charges would be fulfilled, but would have to be deferred for the time being because the Government had given priority to a big improvement in pensions. She also announced that as a result of the annual review of hospital costs, the charges made for pay beds in hospitals would be increased by an average of about 25 per cent. When asked by a Labour M.P. about the ultimate abolition of pay beds, she replied that he knew the policy of the Party and assured him that she had it very much in mind. Furthermore, she announced that because of the concern among senior consultant staff about their contracts, she was setting up a joint working party that not only would study the workload of consultants but also would look into the question of private practice within the Service.

This announcement was welcomed by the British Medical Association, which has been under great pressure from consultants to have their problems adequately reviewed by the

Department of Health. But a leading article in the *British Medical Journal*[4] suggested that Mrs. Castle may be disappointed in what she discovers about private practice, since it does not play a major part in the professional lives of most consultants. On the other hand, it has enabled many to retain a sense of freedom of practice, and many claim that it has helped to maintain high standards of hospital practice. The *British Medical Journal* believes that any question of its prohibition or severe restriction would aggravate a tense medicopolitical situation.

Quite apart from these immediate political pressures on consultants, it must be recognized that the emphasis and orientation of this reorganized National Health Service will be toward the community health services rather than the hospitals. This may well be the right long-term approach to the problem of maintaining the public health, but many consultants will have been disturbed to learn that a report published by the Office of Health Economics[5] has expressed concern that hospital consultants will retain much of their influence on the running of the Service. The report suggests that such an influence could have the unfortunate result of perpetuating the dominance of hospital and curative medicine as opposed to community and preventive medicine. This development could nullify reorganization in such areas as the rehabilitation of the physically handicapped and the mentally sick. The report maintains that the efficient working of the health service now depends on successful teamwork between professional and occupational groups rather than on the leadership of the medical profession; if this fact is not recognized, the full potential contribution of nurses, physiotherapists, pharmacists and administrators may not be realized. In such a complex organization as the National Health Service there are inevitably a large number of professions involved, but there is always a tendency for a swinging pendulum to swing too far. It seems premature to assume that the traditional role of the doctor as the leader of any health-care team is outdated, and equally foolish to allow the hospital service to be run down on the assumption that improved community health services will necessarily make hospitals redundant.

Nevertheless, attitudes are clearly changing, and the newer recruits to the medical profession may not see themselves in such a dominant role as their predecessors. Indeed, Dr. N. W. Chaplin, in his editor's foreword to the 1974 *Hospital and Health Services Year Book*,[6] has referred to these changing attitudes. He points out that until recently, hospitals have been something of a world apart. The feeling of doing a worthwhile job, a sense of dedication and even perhaps the strict discipline and hierarchical structure have been some of the factors producing the peculiar character of hospitals.

The widespread strikes by ancillary staff last year were a new phenomenon and quite uncharacteristic, but Dr. Chaplin fears that in the future, the staffing problems in hospitals may be much more like those in other large organizations and that strikes may become a normal hazard rather than almost an unknown occurrence. Nor does he think that it can be assumed that industrial action would be confined to ancillary staff. The wish to avoid harm to patients would be a deterrent to strikes in the health service, but he does not think that it would be the determining factor because the attitudes of professional and technical staff would reflect those of similar groups in other occupations.

It is surely sad to hear of such predictions. It may be assumed that doctors and nurses would never support any industrial action that would be harmful to patients. Indeed, it might be said that the present situation offers an opportunity for the doctors to establish their claim to retain their role of leadership by acting responsibly in trying to ensure that their patients derive the maximum benefit from the facilities available. No doubt, most doctors are trying to do just that, but many, and particularly those in hospitals, believe that they need rather more official encouragement to do so than they have recently received from the Department of Health.

1. Battistella RM, Chester TE. The 1974 reorganization of the British National Health Service — aims and issues. N Engl J Med 1973; 289:610-615.
2. Leading Article. No fanfares for 1 April. Br Med J 1974; 1:587.
3. Leading Article. Facing the economic facts. Br Med J 1974; 1:467-468.
4. Leading Article. Crisis working parts. Br Med J 1974; 1:532.
5. N.H.S. Re-organisation. London: Office of Health Economics, 1974.
6. The Hospital and Health Services Year Book 1974. Chaplin N, ed. London: Institute of Health Service Administration, 1974.

Political Pressures on an Ailing Health Service

SEPTEMBER 26, 1974

When Aneurin Bevan introduced the National Health Service in 1948, he was able to enlist the cooperation of the senior hospital staff (consultants) only by agreeing that those who wished to continue in part-time practice would be allowed to admit their private patients to pay beds in NHS hospitals. This arrangement was contrary to Socialist doctrine, and although the system worked well for many years, the existence of these pay beds — never more than 1 per cent of the total number of acute-care hospital beds — became a serious political issue, with increasing pressure from health-service trade unions and some Labour politicians to have them closed. During the period of Labour Government (1964 to 1970) the numbers of pay beds were reduced, but when Labour was returned to power in 1974 and Mrs. Barbara Castle became Secretary of State for Health and Social Security, she decided to provoke a confrontation with the hospital consultants on the issue. This confrontation continued for at least two years, during which the morale of the profession was seriously undermined and relations with the government were embittered.

Although the recent attack on private practice was, in many ways, an irrelevant diversion from the real problems of the National Health Service (NHS), it raised a number of vitally important issues. In particular, it emphasized the degree to which the pattern of medicine is being influenced by political pressure. When Mrs. Barbara Castle was appointed Secretary of State at the Department of Health and Social Security after the February election, one of her first actions was to set up a working party to review the form of contract that consultants have with their hospital authorities, and she insisted on including the question of private practice within the scope of the review. Furthermore, she made it clear that she expected the working party to agree on ways of phasing out private beds from NHS hospitals in accordance with Labour Party policy, and hinted that part-time consultants would be offered new whole-time contracts, with some increase in salary, in compensation for their loss of income from private practice. It was not made clear whether existing consultants holding part-time contracts would be allowed to retain them, but although it was conceded that there would still be a private sector in medicine, it was hoped that this would become completely separated from the state system, and that eventually physicians and surgeons engaging in private practice would hold no contract with the NHS.

At present about 50 per cent of the NHS consultants have part-time contracts and, as *The Times*[1] has pointed out, there are good grounds for judging that the present relation between public and private medicine is, on balance, beneficial. The provision of a limited number of private beds in NHS hospitals was a necessary compromise to gain the co-operation of the consultants when the NHS was introduced. The availability of apparently free medicine has done little to diminish the demand for private medicine, which has, on the contrary, become more popular largely because of the expansion of private health-insurance schemes.

But though the private beds in hospitals are few in number, they present an emotional problem for the Labour Party, which has an obsession that they allow the "better off" to jump the waiting-list queues and enjoy the privilege of privacy, at the expense of the NHS patients — at the same time providing a handsome income for the more successful consultants.

Against this must be set the fact that the NHS makes a profit from the charges made to private patients for their accommodation, and that many such patients come from abroad and pay in foreign currency, with benefit to the balance of payments. Furthermore, if consultants were not permitted to engage in private practice, the NHS would have to pay them much more realistic salaries to avert a large increase in medical emigration. But these points were clearly of little interest to the militant trade unionists, who took matters into their own hands and tried to have the private block of the new Charing Cross Hospital closed to private patients and made available to NHS patients free of charge.[2] Their activities spread to many other parts of the country and halted admissions to many private wards. The rather weak rebuke that Mrs. Barbara Castle delivered to those responsible for this disruption of normal services aroused the suspicion that she and her Department were more in sympathy with them than with the inconvenienced private patients. However, the consultants at Charing Cross Hospital took a firm stand on the basis that their clinical management of patients was being challenged by trade-union action, and the British Medical Association supported them by announcing that it would take the unprecedented step of advising consultants to work strictly to their contracts if Mrs. Castle did not intervene personally in the dispute and undertake to maintain the existing provision of government-approved private beds. Eventually she did intervene, and after discussions with both the unions and the British Medical Association and with representatives of the Charing Cross Hospital staff, it was agreed that no permanent change would be made in the number of private beds until the working-party report was available, but temporary closure might be necessary on account of staff shortages and private rooms not being used by private patients would be made available to NHS patients. At the same time she undertook to expedite the publication of the working-party report, and there is little doubt that the unions only agreed to withdraw their sanctions against private patients because they were certain that the report will in fact recommend the phasing out of all private beds from the NHS.

It is not surprising, therefore, that a bitter atmosphere pervades the hospitals that Mrs. Castle has done little to improve. Indeed within a few days of the settlement she was accusing doctors of pursuing jungle tactics and of attempting to bring down the Labour Party. She may well have been angered by the revelation that, in the past, she herself had received treatment in a private room in an NHS hospital, but she chose private treatment for the perfectly good reason that she was a busy government minister at the time and did not want to have her work interrupted. There was nothing dishonorable in this, but as Lord Platt said in the House of Lords,[3] she was not the only person in Britain who wanted such an amenity.

But this issue goes far beyond the question of amenities available to individual patients. Indeed, if the Labour Party proposal to eliminate private practice from the NHS is carried out, it will lead to a radical change in the whole character of the medical profession in Britain that will affect patients, whether public or private, as well as doctors. Such a change was avoided when the NHS was introduced in 1948, and judging from much of the press comment and from the considerable correspondence on the subject, a large body of responsible opinion believes that such a change should be avoided now. Furthermore, any examination of their record of service over the past 25 years would give the part-time consultants a strong claim for the continuation of the present system.

When many of the first generation of part-time NHS consultants were appointed they found serious deficiencies, in terms of both hospital accommodation and equipment and junior staffing arrangements. Many were stimulated by the opportunities that their appointments offered and showed considerable enthusiasm in developing their departments. They were unstinting in the time and energy that they devoted to committee work, and many became involved in plans to adapt old buildings or to build new hospitals. Those who established successful private practices only did so after they had provided a hospital service that the referring general practitioners had judged to be efficient. The development of postgraduate medical centers in district hospitals has been another demand on the time of willing consultants. The majority of the clinical tutors responsible for the organization of teaching in these centers are part-time consultants, and many have raised funds to build their centers with the assistance of influential laymen often met in the course of their private practices.

Instead of attacking these part-time consultants, most of whom have given more hours to their hospitals than their contracts have demanded, the Department of Health and Social Security should be praising them for what they have achieved and should be giving them the tools to get on with their jobs. Similarly, the increasing numbers of potential private patients, insuring themselves so that they will not be a charge on the state when ill, should be encouraged and not denounced as being antisocial. The Department should have the courage to compete with, or at any rate to complement, the facilities in the increasing numbers of private hospitals by providing more private accommodation to the standard of that available in the new Charing Cross Hospital, which has been the focal point of the recent troubles. If only the Department could adopt such an approach, the medical profession would certainly respond, and the NHS might really become the envy of the world.

Unfortunately, there seems little chance that the Department will adopt such an imaginative approach; it is more likely, as already suggested, that two separate systems of health care will eventually evolve — the NHS on the one hand and an entirely independent private sector on the other. Few doctors are happy at such a prospect, partly because they fear the development of a double standard, and partly because of the immense difficulties of financing and building suitable facilities for a greatly enlarged private sector. Nevertheless, there have been discussions about these problems between the private insurance companies concerned and among doctors who would seriously contemplate resignation from the NHS. Already, however, there have been signs of trade-union opposition to the development of private medicine, with reports that technicians belonging to the Association of Scientific, Technical and Managerial Staffs would not work with consultants in any private health service; it has even been suggested that building workers might obstruct the building of new private hospitals. Such attitudes, if translated into action, could clearly threaten the freedom both of patients and of physicians, and it must be hoped that a satisfactory relation between the public and private sectors of medicine will eventually be established.

Meanwhile, the state of the NHS itself continues to cause anxiety. It is sad to see the recent predictions of Dr. N. W. Chaplin[4] — that strikes would soon become a normal hospital hazard — so quickly fulfilled. Thus, although the nurses have agreed to call off their industrial action pending the preliminary report on their pay, due to be published in a few weeks' time, during the last month there have been strikes by technicians, hospital engineers and radiographers, all on account of inadequate pay. The technicians were chiefly those concerned with radiotherapy departments and cardiac and renal units, and several hospitals had to abandon open-heart surgery until the dispute was resolved; the strikes involving engineers closed several hospital laundries, and the admission of patients had to be restricted. Radiographers conducted their campaign by refusing to undertake any routine radiology on selected days, although their militancy has varied in different parts of the country. There is no doubt that all these groups of hospital workers have been poorly paid, and they have had the sympathy of the doctors in their wage claims. At the same time the interruption of normal hospital work by repeated industrial action and the shortage of staff in many departments owing to failing recruitment on account of the poor pay has led to increasing frustration among all those who are trying to maintain a service to patients.

It was because of their growing concern that the British Medical Association called a meeting together with representatives of the dentists and nurses to review the critical state of the finances of the NHS and requested an interview with the Prime Minister, which was granted in late July. At this meeting Mr. Wilson agreed that the representatives of the health professions had given him a somber picture of the deterioration of the NHS. Nevertheless, he rejected the demand that they had made for an immediate £500 million to sustain the NHS, and he also turned down their appeal for an independent inquiry into the method of financing it. On the other hand, he did give an assurance that the government would provide additional funds to meet the cost of inflation and to cover the cost of the pay awards that would have to be made to many groups of hospital staff. These funds will certainly relieve the immediate financial pressure on hospital authorities, but eventually the method of financing the NHS will have to be reviewed. It is difficult to see how a noteworthy increase in available funds will ever be achieved without introducing some form of direct charges for certain selected services — at any rate for those able to pay.

But once again this is a highly emotional political issue that the present government would certainly not wish to raise at a time when an election is probably pending — even though failure to do so may in the end have disastrous effects.

In the past, doctors who have criticized the deficiencies of the NHS have been accused of being alarmist and disloyal; recently, the profession has been criticized by Mrs. Castle for not sounding the alarm bells sooner. However inconsistent these political attitudes may be, there can be no doubt that on this occasion the alarm bells have been sounded loud and clear, and it must be hoped that the government will realize that a radical cure and not just first-aid treatment is required to save the NHS from collapsing.

1. Leading Article. Dictating to the doctors. The Times, July 4, 1974.
2. See "By the London Post," issue of August 29, 1974.
3. Doctors firm on pay beds: parliamentary report. Daily Telegraph, July 20, 1974.
4. The Hospital and Health Services Year Book 1974. Chaplin N, ed. London: Institute of Health Service Adminstration, 1974.

The End of Medical Dominance

APRIL 24, 1975

The image of the doctor has changed in recent years. Previously the physician's dominant role in the care of patients, in medical education, and in many administrative matters was unquestioned. Today in many specialties the care of patients is undertaken by multidisciplinary teams, with decisions concerning even clinical matters being taken after case conferences involving health professionals other than physicians.

In administrative matters the role of the doctor is under even greater challenge. The complexity and cost of modern health care has made change inevitable. Nevertheless, the needs of patients still require doctors to give sound advice to the administrators and to show that they are still worthy of providing leadership.

I was traveling recently with a medical colleague who had been involved in negotiations with representatives of the trade unions whose members had been engaged in disruptive activities in his hospital as part of their campaign to eliminate private practice from the National Health Service (NHS). When I deplored the deterioration in the friendly atmosphere traditionally associated with hospitals that such action reflected, and remarked that I had always enjoyed good personal relations with all members of my hospital staff, whether nurses, porters, technicians or ancillary workers, and that I respected them and hoped that they respected me, he replied that I was in a position of privilege and suspected that my attitude was one of patronage. I assured him that I had never consciously thought of the relation in that way, but after I came across an article entitled "The End of Medical Dominance?"[1] by Dr. Robert Dingwall, a research sociologist in the Medical Research Council Sociology Unit at Aberdeen, my complacency was shaken and certain doubts and fears were aroused.

Dr. Dingwall has identified two main sets of ideas emerging among the ancillary workers and the paraprofessionals in the hospitals that he describes as trade-union consciousness and professional consciousness. These terms do not discriminate neatly between ancillary workers and paraprofessionals since the latter may be just as attracted to trade-union philosophies as the former may be anxious to seek professional certification as ambulance drivers or hospital porters. By trade-union consciousness, Dr. Dingwall refers to the set of demands that are primarily economic, chiefly relating to pay and conditions of service. He believes that in this field, the NHS should be regarded as any other industrial employer and should expect to have to engage in collective bargaining with representatives of its employees. Union strength should be developed to curb the attempts of the employer to minimize labor costs by reducing staffing levels and depressing pay below the rates paid by other employers. In accordance with such a model, employees should be prepared to back up their demands with the normal sanctions of industrial action such as overtime bans, work-to-rule and strikes.

By professional consciousness Dr. Dingwall refers to the set of demands relating primarily to the social standing of the occupations within the medical division of labor. He envisages the establishment of organizations based on the model of doctors' organizations, thereby professionalizing the occupation and enabling it to claim equality of status with the doctors. This setup would lead to a division of medical work into discrete areas with jealously guarded boundaries relating to one another only on a basis of equality. He admits that economic and status issues cannot be separated entirely, and recognizes that the developments that he foresees would tend to promote sectional interests without adequate consideration of the interest of consumers, the patients. He therefore expands his theme to suggest that only a radically democratized health service can serve the medical needs of the public. Thus, he believes that it is wrong for any group to have a blank check on public funds such as the professionals claim. He believes that vast sums are being used in such activities as renal-transplantation programs, to benefit a few patients and boost medical egos while the treatment of many medically less glamorous conditions is being neglected. The total health-service budget in relation to such competing claims as education, welfare and defense is a matter for central government, but Dr. Dingwall suggests that the pattern of local services should be determined by duly elected democratic bodies responsive to the needs and wishes of the people whom they represent. He believes that the recently established community health councils may have a role in this matter, but does not consider them sufficiently democratic in their composition. He suggests that if the trade unions are willing to build on the wider social consciousness expressed in their campaigns over private beds in hospitals, they may have an important part to play in opening up the NHS to public control or in assisting the establishment of the policies of a duly elected government — though he does concede that they remain hampered by their essentially sectional interests. He also stresses the need for a much greater public awareness of health, and points out that if people want good health, they must seek it by the effort of living healthier lives, promoting antipollution measures, eliminating smoking, making factories safer, contributing more in taxation and perhaps even opting for less than the best. But above all it seems that Dr. Dingwall wishes to convey the message that health is too important and too expensive to be left to the professionals.

Certainly the changes that he describes are already taking place, and no doctor could remain complacent after reading his article, but what was the basis for my doubts and fears? Do I doubt the wisdom of suggesting that the doctor should be no more than an equal partner with other health professionals for egotistical reasons or because I still believe he has a unique part to play, and have I any grounds for fearing that the thesis outlined by Dr. Dingwall for democratizing the NHS has any subtle or even sinister political implications?

The suggestion that trade unionists were expressing their social consciousness in campaigning against private patients in NHS hospitals is disturbing because in fact they were victimizing certain hospital patients to try to change agreed arrangements that did not conform with their own political views; this behavior was anarchy, not democracy.

But a national organization is being set up to co-ordinate the activities of the community health councils already established throughout the country under the reorganized NHS. In announcing this step Dr. David Owen[2] of the Department of Health admitted that the health service is already a rationed service, and pointed out that there never would be a government or a country with enough resources to meet all the demands that any nation will make on a national health service. If the community health council can really assume the responsibility of deciding priorities, the professionals should be relieved, but their advice will surely still be required; as potential patients we are all likely to need a physician or even a surgeon at some time, and in the context of the doctor-patient relation, it must be hoped that the role of the doctor will always remain unique. And so we should perhaps not fear too much from the sociologic planners and should do our best to suppress the paranoia that is recognized as being such a dominant feature of the medical character!

---

1. Dingwall R. The end of medical dominance? Health Soc Serv J, January 4, 1975: 21-22.
2. New scheme to make most of rationed NHS. The Times, February 6, 1975.

There Is No Use Chasing an Illusion

JULY 31, 1975

It is always easy to imagine that the grass may be greener elsewhere, and over the years when times have been hard many doctors have emigrated from Britain in search of more satisfying and more rewarding careers than they believed they would enjoy at home. Having had the opportunity of visiting the United States many times, I have been able to observe both the differences and the similarities between our two countries. At times the grass has seemed greener in North America. I was much impressed by a comment made by the late Dr. David Maddison, first dean of the new medical school at Newcastle, New South Wales, that it is no use chasing an illusion.

In the summer of 1975 the medical scene in Britain was particularly gloomy, and the profession remained in dispute with the government and concerned about the state of the National Health Service.

When I left England in May for another brief visit to the United States, there was still intense concern about the National Health Service (NHS) and about the state of the medical profession itself.

As anticipated, the review body that advises the government on doctors' pay had reported to the Prime Minister and recommended substantial pay raises for all doctors working in the NHS. For some groups the increase was about 30 per cent, but took account of the fact that the previous year's award had been restricted by the country's economic circumstances. The government agreed to implement the recommendations and the profession's negotiators advised the doctors to accept the award. Almost simultaneously with the announcement of this decision the British Medical Association advised hospital consultants to end their three months of working strictly to contract, and although the negotiators claimed that this advice was in no way related to the pay award, but the result of further discussions about their term of service with Mrs. Barbara Castle, the Secretary of State for Social Services, there was a strong suspicion that the government might have delayed the award if normal work had not been resumed.

Relations between the British Medical Association and the Hospital Consultants and Specialists Association were severely strained at this time because the latter body was excluded from these discussions with Mrs. Castle, even though it represents the views of about 50 per cent of the senior hospital staff. Nevertheless, although many of its members were reluctant to lift sanctions because they believed that their contracts rather than their rates of pay had been the real issue, normal hospital work was gradually resumed, but many consultants vowed that they would never resume the heavy workload they had previously carried.

It was no surprise that shortly after this uneasy peace had been restored in the hospitals, Mrs. Castle returned to her attack on private practice within the NHS by announcing in Parliament[1] that immediate steps would be taken to close about 500 of the 4500 private beds in NHS hospitals. She explained that this step could be taken without any legislation, and that she would arrange for appropriate legislation to be introduced as soon as possible to eliminate the remaining 4000 beds. Such an announcement had long been anticipated since it has been the declared policy of the Labour Party to separate the private from the public sector in medicine. What was not anticipated was Mrs. Castle's announcement in the same parliamentary statement that she intends to seek new powers over the matter of licensing private hospitals so that she may regulate, more closely than is possible under existing powers, the operation, extent and development of the private sector. She also stated that she wishes to guard against the possible development of undesirable commercial or advertising practices. These remarks have naturally caused great anxiety to those who accepted her earlier assurances that she did not wish to eliminate private practice entirely, but only to separate it from the NHS.

It would seem that Mrs. Castle is now concerned that she might have been the unwilling midwife of a new and flourishing private sector of medicine that would attract many disillusioned physicians from the NHS. Such a sector may yet appear, but she is clearly determined to make that development more difficult. *The Times*[2] certainly interpreted her statement as implying that any major growth in this sector would be looked on with disfavor and in the last resort might lead to the banning of new hospital developments for which private funds are available while NHS building projects are canceled because there is no public money to spare. The *Daily Telegraph*[3] took the view that the announcement revealed the underlying threat to our traditional liberties that may result from universal dependence on the state.

As an alternative a doctor writing a special article in the *Daily Telegraph*[4] suggested that private medicine should be made available not for a few, but for most or even for all by the introduction of universal health insurance, perhaps with a state subsidy or other means of making private medicine available to the poor. Such ideas are probably fanciful in the present political and economic climate in Britain, but in a country that does not yet have a comprehensive health-care system, there are many possibilities to consider, and it is of interest to note that in answering her Tory critics in the debate that followed her statement, Mrs. Castle referred to her recent visit to the United States, where she had noted mounting alarm at the escalating costs of health care under the system of private medical insurance and where she claimed she had encountered feelings of envy and curiosity about the British NHS.

Certainly, I have to admit that my own recent visit to the United States provided no relief from the atmosphere of medical politics that has been so oppressive in Britain in the past year. Some of the problems were similar, and others remarkably different. The recent strike action by young hospital doctors in New York over their conditions of work had a familiar ring although the crisis over malpractice insurance was a manifestation of a problem that is happily a relatively minor one in Britain; indeed, the fact that an annual subscription of £25 to the Medical Defence Union, or £25 to the Medical Protection Society, protects doctors of every specialty against charges of negligence is an indication of just how fortunate the British doctors are as compared with their American colleagues in the matter of litigation.

The public concern over the mounting cost of health care in the United States, of course, is apparent to any visitor, and the medical observer is soon aware that some of the cost is associated with the defensive medicine practiced because of this fear of litigation. The debate about the relative merits of hospital-based medical care versus community care is equally topical on both sides of the Atlantic; it is becoming clear that the latter is not only more economical but in many cases should also be more appropriate. For these reasons it has been actively encouraged in Britain, with renewed emphasis on the place of the general practitioner — preferably working in a group practice — as the source of primary medical care. Similarly, the development of departments of family practice in American medical schools in the hope of recruiting doctors to practice in the community is an encouraging trend in the United States.

I found the attitude of students of these problems to be stimulating, and after I had tried to explain to them the successes and failures of the British NHS, they showed genuine concern that the United States should learn from our mistakes. One serious trap into which I unwittingly fell was in appearing to underestimate the importance of the role of women in medicine. Having qualified a statement that 33 per cent of the medical student intake in Britain are now women, by claiming that this figure seemed fair in view of the proportion of their lives that they are likely to spend in professional practice, I was accused of having made a discriminatory remark! Momentarily at a loss for a suitable reply, I rather feebly (and presumably demonstrating a male chauvinistic tendency) suggested that there was sound biologic evidence for my remark, only to be asked whether in Britain we accepted women medical students who already had children and if not why not — and whether I had taken account of women's excess longevity over men! I was not quick enough to suggest that if women followed the work pattern of men for a generation or two, their life expectancy might drop to that of their male colleagues. At the end of the meeting a pleasant young woman student pointed out one of her contemporaries in her second year helping some of her five children into her motor car! However, in Britain we are well aware of the need to ensure that women doctors are given the opportunity to pursue their careers; indeed, Mrs. Castle has taken the initiative in calling a conference on the subject during the summer, which will be duly reported.

But apart from such unnerving diversions, I still noted the chief concern to be the problem of finding a method of meeting the daunting cost of health care that will be acceptable to the politicians, the public and the profession. And I could only observe that every solution appeared to have an objection. There seems little doubt that any plan based on fee for item of service is open to abuse by the doctors unless it is associated with some method of external audit, and a comprehensive service, such as that in Britain, which is apparently free at the time of use, is open to abuse by the patients. Furthermore, the fully socialized system with the near monopoly employment of salaried doctors as envisaged by the British Labour Party carries the real danger that it will create a drab and shackled medical profession with mediocre standards. Nevertheless, some form of pre-paid health-insurance scheme, perhaps combined with the obligation to pay token fees at the time of use, does seem to be a social need in any civilized country. On the other hand, if there is a message to be found in the British experience it would seem to be that the wholesale takeover of hospitals and the widespread employment of professionals by the state can have serious disadvantages. But as one experienced physician remarked, the fact is that there is no single satisfactory solution; a visiting academic remarked to me last year, as he traveled around the world in search of ideas to help him establish a new medical school, there is no use in chasing an illusion that the grass is greener elsewhere. Each country has its own culture and its own political background; in the matter of health-care delivery each must determine the most appropriate method to ensure that every citizen receives the medical treatment he requires. Strong responsible medical leadership is required to ensure that the profession has a proper role; such leadership has not always been apparent in either of our countries, but it is vital that it should be if professional standards are to be maintained and if the relations between the patients and their doctors are to be protected from the adverse effects of any third party that may become involved.

---

1. Mrs. Castle outlines plans to prevent queue-jumping by private patients. The Times, May 6, 1975.
2. Threat to private medicine. The Times, May 7, 1975.
3. And so to death-bed. Daily Telegraph, May 7, 1975.
4. Partridge A. A cure for the Health Service. Daily Telegraph, May 8, 1975.

A Profession in Distress

JANUARY 29, 1976

The dispute over private practice reached a climax late in 1975, when the Labour Government announced its firm intention to introduce legislation to phase out private practice from National Health Service hospitals and to establish control over the private sector outside the NHS. The British Medical Association claimed that the government had failed to consult the profession adequately, and took the unprecedented step of advising hospital consultants and specialists to treat only emergency cases until the situation was resolved; mass resignation from the NHS was also considered. At the same time, the junior hospital doctors were also in dispute over their pay; they too had imposed an overtime ban and were working a strictly 40-hour week. Most doctors were reluctant to become involved in this kind of industrial action, but unfortunately the image of the profession did become tarnished as a result of the incident and the profession suffered a certain loss of its self-respect, even though it was reacting to extreme provocation.

At the time of this writing the medical profession in Britain is in more serious conflict with the government than ever before. The 19,000 junior doctors in the hospital service are working a strict 40-hour week, and the consultants and specialists have been advised by the British Medical Association to treat emergency cases only, while the Hospital Consultants and Specialists Association is calling for mass resignations from the National Health Service (NHS).

Two separate issues are involved. The junior doctors who have been negotiating the terms of a new contract with the Department of Health for more than a year have been told that any further monetary concession from the government would involve a breach of the £6.00 pay limit that has been accepted by all other workers, and this discrepancy cannot be allowed. They disputed the calculations made by the Department of Health, claimed that they had been misled and, when final deadlock was reached, resorted to industrial action.

The issue with the consultants is much more a matter of principle and arose when the Queen's speech[1] at the opening of Parliament included a definite statement that legislation would be introduced during the forthcoming session to phase out private practice from the NHS hospitals and to establish control over the private sector of medicine outside the NHS. The statement was regarded as a direct threat to the freedom of practice for individual consultants and a threat to the choice of doctor by the patient; in spite of any reassurance from the Secretary of State for the Department of Health, Mrs. Barbara Castle, it was believed that the ultimate objective of the present administration is the total abolition of private medicine.

The Royal Colleges and faculties, being chiefly concerned with the maintenance of standards in medicine, could not support the restriction of the services of the profession in the way proposed, but they deplored the refusal of the government to show any willingness to consult the profession in a meaningful way. Sir Rodney Smith, president of the Royal College of Surgeons, acting as spokesman for all the Royal Colleges, requested a meeting with the Prime Minister to appeal for his intervention.

Meanwhile, the effect of the restricted services has varied in different parts of the country, but few hospitals in England and Wales have been working normally, and in many, whole departments have been closed. The long-term effects cannot be forecast, but it is clearly not possible to believe that patients will not suffer; this must surely be a matter for concern to every member of the profession, since there must be some measure of collective responsibility in the present situation.

On the whole the public has been remarkably sympathetic to the junior doctors, recognizing that they do work long hours, but *The Times*[2] pointed out that they have mounted a direct challenge to the government's incomes policy that the government really has to resist. On the other hand, *The Times* believes that the consultants, who can so easily be represented as concerned only with the protection of privilege and their own incomes, are better justified in their actions.

The issue is to some extent symbolic, but it is a symbol that justifies the importance attached to it as a test of the government's intentions toward the profession and the health service. Private beds constitute only 1 per cent of the beds in NHS hospitals, and they permit private patients to gain small advantages in the timing and privacy of their treatment. These comforts do not amount to privilege of a kind that it is reasonable to regard as offensive, and any abuse could be eliminated without abandoning the system. But these few beds are of some importance to the NHS: they bring in a small income and allow effective savings on consultants' salaries; they keep consultants who have private work in hospitals within reach of their NHS patients; they ensure a basically common standard of care for patients of both kinds; and they reduce the wasteful duplication of facilities. Furthermore, in many parts of the country there are no private beds available outside the local NHS hospital, and the government has made no proposals that would guarantee the incomes of the doctors who depend upon them.

The Times also points out that many doctors who have no private work attach great importance to the existence of these private beds, believing that private practice provides a safeguard to professional independence and a protection against exploitation. The government's intentions toward private beds are regarded as an indication of its intentions toward private practice in general and toward medical services as a whole.

It is conceded that the government has the right to give legal effect to the proposals in the Labour Party manifesto, but it has no right to assume that those who work for it will accept the changes involved. As an employer, it is foolish for the government to make unilateral changes in their terms of work that vital employees reject and regard as crucially important; to legislate such a change at a time when the morale of the service is subject to severe stresses for other reasons is doubly foolish. Even a victory in such a struggle would be pyrrhic if it left such disaffection behind that doctors opted in large numbers to leave the service or the country for good. Ultimately, doctors are not only the most essential workers in the NHS but also the ones least dependent on it.

The Times believes that the course that would offer the best chance of success in resolving the crisis with the least sacrifice of ideology and face would be to refer the matter to the Royal Commission on the NHS as originally suggested by the profession.

Other comment in the lay press has not been so favorable to the doctors. *The Sunday Times*[3] claimed that in its present militant posture, the medical profession has lost a lot of public respect and may lose its self-respect as well. The withdrawal of services from patients by organized groups of doctors would have been unimaginable in the recent past, and *The Sunday Times* thought that junior doctors and consultants alike were on the brink of losing the special respect and status that society had previously granted them by virtue of the high standards of conduct that their profession demanded of them.

Certainly, there are many in the profession who are seriously concerned about the changing image of the doctor in society, but it must be realized that the change has been at any rate partly determined by the pressures being exerted on the doctor as a professional in a political environment.

This problem was examined recently by Hugh Dudley, professor of surgery at St. Mary's Hospital, London,[4] who considered the definition of a profession. It might be regarded as a group of individuals largely, if not solely, concerned with preserving its own status. More idealistically, it is a collection of people who, while recognizing their individuality, still think that there are some binding principles that transcend self-interest. Medicine has strong self-interest, but at the same time it is firmly lashed to the ship of society if not to the barque of state. Dudley believes that because of these two allegiances it is making fair to destroy itself.

Self-interest generates a desire to preserve the status quo, and self-concern corrupts debates away from any long-term consideration of the principles on which social institutions such as the NHS are based toward the short-term expedients of what is good for individual professionals. Part of a profession's self-maintenance lies in its public image; medicine in the past has enjoyed a unique position because of the naked power with which it was credited in relation to life or death, and sickness or health. Such quasi-magical authority cannot be sustained if in the marketplace individual members of the profession are seen to behave in a manner showing that they have feet of clay. Dudley thus believes that the declining standards of which many leaders of the profession complain are partly the result of a loss of confidence by the public, the press and the politicians in the profession's rectitude and personal disinterest.

Another characteristic of the professions is their axiomatic amateurism when it comes to tackling anything new. When society changes, a profession is likely to be left behind because of its inward-looking thought. Once it belatedly recognizes change there is a violent reaction, usually accompanied by rhetorical statements about ill defined principles.

In medicine the reaction to change has been to invoke clinical freedom and its erosion as a stopping-point in negotiation — though exactly what clinical freedom is remains largely unspecified. Dudley thinks it is partly the right to do as one pleases with individual problems and partly the privilege to defy social regulations that could lead (at least in theory) to the resolution of inequality as seen from a point of view other than that of those who demand self-determination. More fundamentally, it might incorporate a right to dissent, which is a characteristic of universities but a doubtful attribute of professions.

In his concluding remarks Dudley feared he could smell suicide in the air, for medicine as a profession, but he was not sure what could be done to prevent it. He could only suggest that the profession should take stock of its own raison d'être to see how it can or should be modified and finally to come up with some practical proposals for meshing professional ideals with public expectations.

Sir Harry Platt, the senior living past president of the Royal College of Surgeons, also reflected on the state of the profession in a remarkable speech that he delivered at a dinner given in his honor to mark his retirement from the editorship of the British edition of *Modern Medicine*. He admitted that he was 89 and therefore had had a long life, but he assumed that his longevity was due to some genetic accident. To have lived through three generations had given him an unusual experience; he had no regrets that he had been a doctor, and he was glad that he could still take an active interest in surgery, which dominates medicine. But he was sad to see our beloved profession in such a state of turmoil. He recalled how Lord Keynes had defined the place of an artist in society as being "a public servant, but his own master." This was surely how a physician should regard himself. He should not be a servant of any government local or central, but of all the people and available at all times to those seeking his service. As Mr. Justice Holmes would have said, "The decision will depend on a judgement or intuition more subtle than any articulate major premise."

1. Debate on the Queen's speech — NHS. Br Med J 1975; 4:531.
2. The medical contract. The Times, November 27, 1975.
3. Medicine debased. The Sunday Times, November 23, 1975.
4. Dudley HAF. A profession destroying itself? Lancet 1975; 2:972-973.

Political Vicissitudes of the NHS

JUNE 24, 1976

When Mr. James Callaghan succeeded Mr. Harold Wilson as Prime Minister in 1976, he replaced Mrs. Barbara Castle with Mr. David Ennals as the Secretary of State at the Department of Health and Social Security. The relief of the doctors was somewhat tempered by Mr. Ennals' remark that although his style might be different, his principles were the same as those of Mrs. Castle. All the same, this change did relieve some of the tensions that had developed between the doctors and the politicians. It seemed an opportune moment to reflect on the way that the personalities of the Ministers of State and Secretaries of State had affected the fortunes of the National Health Service and those working in it.

———————

At present, when the new Prime Minister, Mr. James Callaghan, has replaced Mrs. Barbara Castle with Mr. David Ennals as Secretary of State at the Department of Health and Social Security, it is appropriate to reflect on the way in which the character of British medical practice has been affected by the attitudes and policies of the politicians. Broad policy is, of course, decided by the governing party, but the personal characteristics of individual health ministers have greatly influenced the manner in which agreed policies have been implemented, and the relations that they have had with the health professions have greatly influenced the working of the National Health Service (NHS). Thus, although Aneurin Bevan had the

fiercest of arguments with the doctors at the time he was preparing to introduce the NHS in 1948 he gained their respect for
his enthusiasm, sincerity and ability to keep his side of a bar-
gain once it had been struck. Nevertheless, the legislation that
he introduced brought about the greatest changes that had
ever taken place in the practice of medicine in this country. He
would undoubtedly have liked to introduce a whole-time salaried service both in family practice and in the hospitals, but he
had to accept a compromise. The family doctors insisted on
remaining self-employed independent contractors, a status
they were able to preserve by accepting the capitation-fee system; the hospital consultants insisted that their independence
could be ensured only if they were allowed to elect part-time
contracts with the NHS and permitted to engage in private
practice. This vital point was conceded by Bevan, who agreed
that 1 per cent of the beds in the NHS should be available for
private patients. These concessions were largely responsible
for the spirit of good will that sustained the NHS for many
years. On the one hand, the politicians respected the independence of the medical profession, and for their part the doctors
and nurses worked hard and amicably with their colleagues in
the ancillary health professions to render a good service to their
patients.

Subsequent health ministers have had to grapple with recurring disputes about pay and conditions of service, career prospects and available resources, but ways and means of resolving
most of these difficulties were eventually found. It appeared
that the unlikely partnership between the state and the health
professions would prove to be of lasting benefit to the great
majority of the nation's sick.

Iain Macleod, the son of a family doctor, was one of the early
Tory ministers responsible for the NHS. His own background
helped him to recognize the importance of primary care; Enoch
Powell, the first health minister to make a thorough assessment
of the hospital service, was responsible for the plan[1] to provide

a network of properly equipped district general hospitals throughout the country. He doubted the wisdom of ever having embarked on a health service that provided apparently free treatment at the time of need, but recognized that it would be politically impossible to reverse the deal. At the same time he warned that with such a system, the demand would be insatiable and that some form of rationing of health care would eventually become necessary. His inscrutable character, apparently lacking in warmth, did not endear him to the doctors; it was the Labour health minister, Kenneth Robinson, a lawyer by profession and, like Iain Macleod, the son of a family doctor, who seemed to establish the most satisfactory working relation with the medical profession. Certainly, he came under political pressure to investigate complaints that the private sector within the NHS was being abused by some part-time consultants. As a result, a small reduction in the number of private beds was made, but there was no change in the principle originally agreed to with Aneurin Bevan. Furthermore, Mr. Robinson did much to consolidate the achievements of the NHS and tried to balance the claims of the still expanding hospital service against the competing demands of family practice; he created the impression that he was genuinely concerned about the welfare of the NHS and of all those working in it. He was in fact the last Minister of Health, for he was succeeded in 1968 by Richard Crossman, who as Secretary of State at the newly created Department of Health and Social Security was responsible not only for health but also for all the Social Services, with separate ministers of State assisting him in his task.

Many believe that this change may have been a retrograde step for the NHS, which was somehow deprived of a spokesman with undivided loyalties. Certainly, it would take a person of massive intellect and strong determination to master the intricacies of so large an organization as the Department of Health and Social Security. It was during Crossman's tenure of office that plans to reorganize the NHS were conceived. It was Sir Keith Joseph, Secretary of State at the Department in the Heath Government, however, who was responsible for introducing the legislation that provided for the unification of the family-practitioner service, the hospital service and the local-authority medical services.

Ever since the beginning of the NHS there had been some criticism of its tripartite structure, and the concept of unification of the whole service with great emphasis on managerial efficiency was undoubtedly attractive to Sir Keith, whose previous experience was chiefly in the company boardroom. Indeed, he adopted the plans enthusiastically and called upon the doctors to accept the challenge of becoming more directly involved in decision making since one of the major features of this plan would be to delegate responsibility downward, though this change would be matched by a requirement that accountability would be directed upward! But, in fact, the reorganization that took effect on April 1, 1974, has probably created more problems than it solved. There has been a huge increase in the number of administrators, partly owing to the creation of a whole new administrative tier of area health authorities, so that doctors and administrators alike have been frustrated by ever-increasing delays in decision making, rather than the reverse promised by the proponents of reorganization.

Politicians often remark that they rarely remain in office long enough to implement the policies that they have planned. Sir Keith Joseph may therefore have regretted that because of the defeat of the Tory Party at the general election in February, 1974, he was out of office when the reorganization became effective. For her part, Mrs. Barbara Castle, who succeeded him, was perhaps unfortunate in finding that her first task was to overcome the major problems created by the reorganization. If she had set about this activity in a constructive manner she might have retained the good will of the medical profession, but unfortunately she introduced into the Department of Health and Social Security an atmosphere of political motivation that had not seriously affected the NHS for many years. Thus, it soon became clear that her major preoccupation was to eliminate private practice from the NHS. In spite of the agreement between Aneurin Bevan and the doctors the Labour Party has long been determined to achieve this aim; indeed, the more extreme elements in the Party would like to see private practice banned altogether, even outside the NHS.

When she was appointed, Mrs. Castle came under pressure from the trades unions, particularly those with members working in the hospitals, to expedite the introduction of legislation that would enable her to separate private practice from the NHS, and she duly declared her intention of doing so. This announcement brought her into immediate conflict with the doctors, with whom she never succeeded in establishing any satisfactory dialogue. It was therefore hoped that her departure from the Department and the appointment of Mr. Ennals as her successor might provide the opportunity for establishing better relations.

Unfortunately, there appears to be no such hope in the immediate future because the introduction of the Health Services Bill to separate private practice from the NHS was imminent at the time of the change, and Mr. Ennals declared that although his style might be different, his principles were the same as those of Mrs. Castle and he had no intention of tinkering with the bill that she had prepared. This bill,[2] which Mr. Ennals introduced on April 12, provides for the closure of 1000 private beds in NHS hospitals within six months of its becoming law, and for the establishment of an independent Health Services Board to plan the phased closure of the remaining 3500 beds. On the other hand, the bill confirms that the right of part-time consultants to continue to practice privately outside the NHS will be preserved and that the closure of the remaining beds will depend on the availability of alternative accommodation in the private sector. Any proposals to build new private hospitals for acute medicine or surgery will require authorization by the Board if their bed complement should exceed 100 in London or 75 elsewhere. The bill also includes a provision that common waiting lists for hospital admission shall be established for NHS and private patients to ensure that the date of admission is determined only on the basis of medical priority.

Although the terms of the bill have been modified in the light of negotiations that took place last year, the principle of eliminating private practice from the NHS is still opposed by the British Medical Association, the Hospital Consultants and Specialists Association and the newly formed Independent Hospital Group. This opposition has arisen partly because the proposed elimination is regarded as a unilateral breach of an agreement, partly because it is clearly politically motivated and partly because the opposition parties genuinely believe that the existence of a small private sector within the NHS has been of benefit to the Service. It is also feared that even present proposals constitute a threat to the independence of the profession, especially because a motion calling for the banning of all private practice was carried at the Labour Party conference last year.

However, it must now be hoped that the different style that Mr. Ennals has hinted that he will bring to the Department of Health and Social Security will somehow help to repair the damage caused by the events of the last two years, which alienated the good will of many doctors, to the great detriment of the Service.

Nevertheless, the many vicissitudes that the NHS has experienced as the result of repeated changes of direction by political parties and ministers with widely differing personal characteristics must surely suggest that some way should be found of ensuring that any nation's health service should be protected from changing political winds. No one has suggested just how this goal could be achieved, but it is possible that the idea of the independent Health Services Board, which is to be responsible for the monitoring of private practice within the NHS, could be developed so that it might have a far larger sphere of responsibility and might even develop into a health-service corporation responsible for administering the NHS without the direct political control that now exists.

1. A hospital plan for England and Wales (Parliamentary Command Paper No. 1604). London: Her Majesty's Stationery Office, 1962.
2. Bill to phase out NHS pay-beds. Br Med J 1976; 1:1024.

How Many Doctors?

At times in Britain a deficiency of numbers has been forecast; at other times there have been forecasts of medical unemployment. Both fears could have substance, because the real figure that needs to be determined is the number of doctors that a country can afford to train and subsequently to employ. Some of the many facets of this difficult problem are considered in these two articles.

The estimation of the number of doctors required to meet the medical needs of a country is a notoriously difficult and apparently unreliable exercise. Thus, in this country a committee[1] was set up in 1955 under the chairmanship of Sir Henry Willink "to estimate on a long-term basis and with due regard to all relevant considerations, the number of medical practitioners likely to be engaged in all branches of the profession in the future and the consequential intake of medical students required." These terms of reference related to the requirements of England, Scotland and Wales, and the committee took account of the emigration of British graduates and the immigration of graduates from elsewhere.

The committee recognized two views at the time: the view that too few doctors were being trained to meet the requirements of an expanding and comprehensive health service; and the opposing view that too many doctors were being trained to fill the likely number of available posts. The committee found great difficulty in determining which of these opposing views was likely to be more nearly correct. A review of the various registers available indicated that, in 1955, there were about 53,260 doctors in active practice in Britain; on the basis of the age ranges of these doctors and appropriate actuarial calculations, it was estimated that the annual intake of students that would be necessary to maintain the same number of doctors would range from 1150 in the years 1955–1960 to 1260 in the years 1970–1975.

It then carried out further calculations to estimate the likely increase in numbers of doctors that might be required. In general practice this estimation depended on a reduction in the permitted maximum number of patients on the lists of individual practitioners, which at the time was 4000 for a single-handed practice, 5300 for a member of a partnership and 2400 for an employed assistant. In fact, although there was a wide variation in different parts of the country in 1955, the average number of patients for each general practitioner was no more than 2283; to reduce that number to 2000, an additional 600 general practitioners would have been required. In the hospitals there were about 10,000 permanent senior staff members in 1955, and it was estimated that an annual expansion rate of about 160 would be required over the ensuing 20 years. Also, about 10,000 junior doctors were employed in hospitals in 1955, a number that the committee thought would also increase by about 160 each year for 10 years and then by 80 each year after 1965.

The numbers of doctors employed in private practice, in university and research posts and by local authorities, government departments, industry and the armed forces were also considered.

The effects of immigration and emigration were also studied, and it seemed that, in 1955, there was a net loss of about 200 doctors from Britain, but it was estimated that this loss would be reduced to 160 by 1960 and to 50 by 1971. It was noted that, in 1955, the proportion of women students being admitted to medical schools was about one fifth of the total intake in accordance with the recommendations of the Goodenough Committee.[2]

In the light of all these figures, and taking account of the fact that there would be a planned reduction in the number of doctors in the armed forces, the Willink Committee estimated that the number of new medical graduates required would be 1830 in the years 1955–1960, 1785 in the years 1960–1965, 1635 in the years 1965–1970 and 1645 in the years 1970–1971. In the years 1955–1961 it was estimated that the output of the medical schools of the United Kingdom, including Northern Ireland, would be about 1855.

The committee therefore concluded that in 1957, when its report was published, the medical schools were not producing too many doctors but that after 1961 they would be doing so and a reduction in student intake by about one tenth was recommended.

Within a few years, however, a new report[3] on the medical staffing of hospitals was followed by a large expansion of junior hospital posts and a much smaller increase in the number of consultant posts with full staff status. This development led to a widening of the base of the pyramidal staffing structure of the hospital service, and it was because there were insufficient numbers of British graduates to fill these junior posts that it was possible to absorb a large number of foreign medical graduates (FMG's) who came primarily for training but found that they were often doing no more than meet the service requirements of the hospitals. At the same time many British graduates were unable to obtain senior appointments on completion of their training, and the net loss by medical emigration was soon far in excess of the modest estimates of the Willink Committee. The Royal Commission on Medical Education,[4] under the chairmanship of Lord Todd, was then appointed; when it reported in 1966 it recommended that the output of medical schools should be increased to 4000 by 1980. But now, once again, the question of medical manpower is under close scrutiny. The latest figures available[5] indicate that in September, 1975, there were about 65,000 doctors in active practice in Britain: 25,000 were in general practice, 4000 were employed in the armed forces, occupational medicine and community medicine, and the remaining 36,000 were working in the hospitals, 20,000 being junior hospital doctors and 16,000 consultants or specialists holding permanent hospital appointments.

In the hospitals, 9000 of the junior hospital staff and 2000 of the senior staff were overseas graduates, and 2000 of the general practitioners were also FMG's.

In spite of this present dependence on overseas graduates, which it is anticipated will be reduced, there is once again increasing concern that too many doctors are being trained and that medical unemployment may be seen in the 1980's. This view was expressed by Sir Cyril Clarke,[6] immediate past-president of the Royal College of Physicians of London. He recognized that it was government policy to increase the output from British medical schools so that we should no longer be dependent on overseas doctors, but he suspected that the country would remain in economic disarray for some years and thought it unwise to count on much growth within the National Health Service (NHS). He wondered, therefore, whether there would be careers available for additional young people in a health service when expansion both of the hospital service and in general practice was likely to be limited by lack of money. He was also concerned about the implications of the free movement of doctors within the European Economic Community, with every member country being obliged to recognize the medical degrees granted by the universities in fellow member countries. Sir Cyril appreciated that this requirement would widen the opportunities for practice for British medical graduates, but pointed out that nearly every other European country is in similar danger of training too many doctors, many of whom would be English speaking and might well seek employment in Britain. Sir Cyril admitted that the increasing number of women medical students, who now constitute about 40 per cent and could eventually make up about 50 per cent of the intake, is a complicating factor because it is not possible to estimate how many will be fully employed in practice. Nevertheless, he thought that there was a case for making a downward revision in the number of students being accepted into the medical schools.

He also questioned the present staffing structure in the hospitals, particularly the consultant system, which the *British Medical Journal*[7] recognizes as the most atypical aspect of British medicine. He believes that a specialist career grade should be introduced between the senior-registrar (senior-resident) grade and consultant, so that fully trained physicians and surgeons could have the opportunity of taking full clinical responsibility without having to wait several years for a consultant vacancy, as they may have to do at present. This situation would be in line with practice in other parts of the world and would reduce the greatly inflated ranks of the so-called junior hospital doctors, but the medical profession in this country has always resisted the creation of any subconsultant grade, chiefly because it has feared that there would be a considerable pay differential between consultants and "specialists" and that, for financial reasons, the Department of Health would then try to keep the more highly paid senior consultant establishment small.

At present this is perhaps rather an irrelevant point, for the combined effect of the new contracts for junior hospital staff with a basic 40-hour week and overtime payments and the government's pay policy has led to a gross distortion and even a reversal of pay differential between senior registrars and junior consultants. It must be assumed that this anomaly will be corrected, but nevertheless in any state-controlled health service, it is inevitable that career structure and the allocation

of medical manpower will be dependent on negotiations between the profession and the government, which has to provide
the finance and must be concerned with cost effectiveness.

It is interesting, therefore, that Sir Cyril also pointed out
that an effective health-education program might reduce the
number of doctors required and that the increasing use of
adequately trained nurses and ancillary workers could reduce
the doctor's workload, although he recognized that this is a
sensitive area because the profession already believes that its
responsibilities are being eroded.

The public debate on this topic was extended after *The Times*
published a leading article[8] in which it suggested that if there
were no financial constraints, it might be claimed that it would
be scarcely possible to produce too many doctors, but public
thrift must imply that output should be measured by the pro-
spective needs of the health service. One correspondent[9] with a
concern for the needs of developing countries suggested that
Britain should follow their example and incorporate into the
NHS a new breed of paramedics costing less to train, providing
easier and more appropriate access to basic health care and
having more modest professional aspirations. Not surprisingly,
Dr. Elston Grey-Turner,[10] secretary of the British Medical
Association, was quick to reject this proposal, pointing out that
the Association had already advised the Royal Commission on
the NHS that "the introduction of physician assistants, nurse
practitioners or feldshers would not be in the best interest of
patients."

A sociologist, Mr. Rudolf Klein,[11] in his usual incisive and
provocative manner, looked at the problem in a different context, pointing out that the anxiety about a surplus of doctors
had arisen because views about Britain's economic prospects
have changed since the present training program was drawn
up. Thus, the case for using less skilled labor as a substitute for
doctors or other professionals is that the former is cheaper, but
this is on the assumption that traditional differentials are invio-

late. One answer to a threatened surplus of professionals, therefore, would be to reduce their relative earnings so as to make it possible to employ more of them. This is certainly an ingenious argument but one hardly likely to commend itself to the medical profession.

Having tried to trace the origins of the various forecasts and revised forecasts of the medical-manpower requirements in Britain, one realizes, of course, that the number of doctors being trained in any country has international as well as national implications. Thus, a medical qualification has been regarded as a valid ticket of entry into the world market for doctors, and the migration of doctors from one country to another has depended both on financial incentives and on the professional opportunities available. As the richer countries expand the ranks of their home-trained doctors, the need to import doctors from poorer countries will diminish, and those in need of health care in those poorer countries should eventually benefit. But this development will depend on the extent to which these countries can afford to support their health service; in a recent article in *New Society*[12] on the problem of the migration of professionals from one country to another, Oscar Gish and Martin Godfrey point out that, throughout the world, most illness does not require the attention of highly trained doctors. Nevertheless, behind the present training of doctors is the assumption that health care must be based on the availability of professionals with many years of basic medical education followed by more years of specialist training. It is therefore likely that the pressure to consider the role of the ancillary worker and the paramedic in health-care delivery will continue.

Meanwhile, however, it does seem essential that whatever the number of medical students eventually admitted into medical schools, those who are accepted and graduate should have reasonable expectations of being appointed to posts that will offer them the opportunity to practice the skills for which they have been trained. If more doctors are being trained than a country can afford to support, there will be medical graduates who are either frustrated or unemployed. To avoid this situation, it becomes increasingly important for each country to assess its own needs in terms of medical manpower, and in a country where there is a state-controlled health service that is virtually the monopoly employer of doctors, it is vital that the calculations should be more nearly correct than in the British experience of the past 25 years.

1. Report of the Committee to Consider the Future Numbers of Medical Practitioners and the Appropriate Intake of Medical Students. London: Her Majesty's Stationery Office, 1957.

2. Interdepartmental Committee in Medical Schools (The Goodenough Committee). London: His Majesty's Stationery Office, 1944.

3. Report of the Joint Working Party on Medical Staffing Structure of the Hospital Service. London: Her Majesty's Stationery Office, 1961.

4. Royal Commission on Medical Education: Report 1965-68. London: Her Majesty's Stationery Office, 1968.

5. Present and projected numbers of medical students and doctors. Br Med J 1977; 1:659.

6. Clarke CA. Wrong ways to choose right medics. The Times, Higher Education Supplement, January 21, 1977.

7. Medical manpower. Br Med J 1977; 1:465.

8. How many doctors for the eighties? The Times, March 14, 1977.

9. Doctor manpower. The Times, March 18, 1977.

10. Doctor manpower. The Times, March 23, 1977.

11. Doctors and the economy. The Times, March 24, 1977.

12. Gish O, Godfrey M. Why did the doctor cross the road? New Society, March 17, 1977.

The Numbers Game

Training doctors is an expensive exercise, and in most countries the major part of the cost of doing so is borne by the state (treasury or exchequer). In Britain, it is now estimated that the cost of producing a doctor is about £40,000. It is therefore important for each country to know how many doctors it requires, but this has always been difficult to determine.

In 1970[1] the government decided that the medical-school intake in Britain should be increased so that about 4000 doctors would graduate annually from 1980 onward. Delays in the expansion of medical-school building have made it impossible to reach this target as early as was hoped, but the validity of the data on which the target was based has been questioned. The Department of Health and Social Security has just published a new document entitled *Medical Manpower: The next twenty years.*[2]

As previously mentioned in the *Journal*,[3] many earlier efforts to forecast the number of doctors required in Britain at some future date have proved to be inaccurate, and it is not surprising that initial reaction to the publication of this new document was one of skepticism. But the introduction to this paper points out that the document does not attempt to assess the total demand for doctors in future years, but rather to set out, as a basis for debate, the assumptions underlying the present manpower policy and to identify areas where further study or research is required.

It is indicated that all developed countries have had difficulty in determining the right number of doctors to train, but all over the world the ratio of doctors to population, or doctor-patient quotient, has shown a steady increase over time. The Royal Commission on Medical Education, under the chairmanship of Lord Todd,[4] found that in Britain this quotient has been rising at the rate of 1.25 per cent per year since the early part of the century. On the other hand, comparisons between different countries show no clear relation between the number of doctors per head of population and any of the conventional indexes of the state of a nation's health, such as perinatal mortality or life expectancy, so that although a rising doctor-patient quotient may indicate how societies choose to spend their money, it may not in fact be a very clear indication of their need for doctors.

In attempting to forecast future needs in medical manpower the Department of Health and Social Security points out that two approaches are possible — the first is based on an expert assessment of a theoretical need for medical care, and the second is by extrapolation of past trends. The former method tends to produce unrealistically high estimates, and the latter makes no provision for future changes in policy. Furthermore, the variety of tasks undertaken by doctors is now so great that it is doubtful whether the service that they provide in different branches of the profession can be compared in any quantitative way.

And so the present discussion paper has been prepared within the working assumption that the method of delivering health care in Britain will not change radically over the next 20 years and that over this period there will inevitably be restraints caused by some limitation on available resources.

In trying to determine whether the country could afford to increase the number of doctors, the Todd Commission assumed that the proportion of the gross national product devoted to health would be maintained and concluded that if a real annual growth of 3 per cent in gross national product could be achieved, it should certainly be possible to sustain a growth of 1.5 per cent per year in the number of doctors.

Turning to the question of the demand for doctors, the paper points out that this demand could be modified by demographic changes, correction of maldistribution, changes in the organization of medical practice and improvement in the services provided. One of the main reasons for the inaccurate forecasting by the Willink Committee[5] of the number of doctors required was the rapid growth of population that occurred after it reported. There is still a wide margin of uncertainty about the likely fertility rates of women during the next 20 years, but the greatest demand for medical care comes from the elderly, and all those who will be 60 or more by the end of the century have already been born, so that all projections agree on the numbers in this age group. Clearly, the care of the elderly may create a demand for more doctors. The British Geriatric Society has proposed a target of three specialist geriatricians for every 200,000 population with an average proportion of elderly people — which is 375 more geriatricians than practice in Britain at present.

Psychiatry and pediatrics are other specialties in which there is a need for expansion if the community is to have the kind of service thought to be desirable. The demand for anesthesiologists continues to grow, not only because of the increasing demands of the surgeons but also because of the work that anesthesiologists now carry out in pain clinics and intensive-care units and in providing an epidural analgesia service for the obstetricians.

But the total number of doctors needed could be affected by changes in the health-care delivery system, both inside and outside the hospital. Thus, with the continuing trend for general practitioners to work from health centers or group-practice premises there has already been a considerable redistribution of work between medical and nonmedical staff, with consequent economy of the doctor's time. In the hospitals the main problem is the imbalance between the large number of junior doctors in training grades and the much smaller number of permanent specialist or consultant posts. This situation has only persisted for so long because at least half the junior staff have been foreign medical graduates, the majority of whom will not seek a permanent career in Britain.

The increased medical-school intake will ensure that eventually the country will be self-reliant for junior hospital staff, but when this development comes about and virtually all hospital training posts are filled by British graduates, the majority of whom intend to stay in the country, the ratio of career posts to training posts will clearly need to change so that these young people may have reasonable expectations of being appointed to posts that will offer them the opportunity to practice the skills for which they have been trained. The role of women in medicine is another complicating factor when numbers are being considered. At present women make up 35 per cent of the medical-student population, and by 1985 their numbers are likely to reach parity with those of men. Recent figures show that there is a substantial increase in the amount of time that medical women are spending in professional activities; it seems likely that this trend will continue. At the same time, when half the medical-school output consists of women, the proportion of their time that they are prepared to spend in the practice of their profession will possibly become the most important factor in determining the total number of students who should be admitted.

Meanwhile, however, the Department of Health and Social Security paper suggests that if the medical-school intake remained at 4000 a year until the end of the century, the growth in total numbers of doctors without net immigration would still be less than the limit of 1.5 per cent per annum that seemed financially possible. This situation would mean that resources could be available to employ the additional doctors and to provide the necessary support facilities, but whether it would be the best use of resources would be a question of priorities. Whether or not there is an increase in the number of doctors, the paper does point out that, over the next 20 years, one of the major tasks will be to persuade doctors to train for the specialties where they are most needed and to be prepared to work in the parts of the country that are understaffed at present. It is difficult to persuade a young graduate keen to become a vascular surgeon in a well-equipped busy center that he really should consider becoming a geriatrician in a small town in the country. Few entrants to medical school have any clear ideas of their plans for their careers or even of the options open to them. Perhaps more emphasis should be placed on informing students of their career prospects early in their course, obviously with great stress on the challenge of geriatric medicine.

1. Hansard, Vol 806, Column 443. November 18, 1970.
2. Medical manpower: the next twenty years. London: Her Majesty's Stationery Office, 1978.
3. Lister J. How many doctors? N Engl J Med 1977; 296:1215-1217.
4. Royal Commission on Medical Education: Report 1965-68. London: Her Majesty's Stationery Office, 1968.
5. Report of the Committee to Consider the Future Numbers of Medical Practitioners and the Appropriate Intake of Medical Students. London: Her Majesty's Stationery Office, 1957.

Backward or Forward?

Successive Ministers of Health and Secretaries of State for Health and Social Services have tried to leave some tangible evidence of their period of office.

Mr. David Ennals, who succeeded Mrs. Barbara Castle, tried hard to repair the rift that had developed between politicians and the medical profession. He also tried hard to identify the most important priorities for the National Health Service. He was convinced that there should be more investment in community health services and rather less in the more expensive hospital service. He believed that savings could be made in hospital expenditure if the medical profession would take an active part in pursuing a vigorous policy of efficiency and economy. His views were expressed in a booklet published by the Department of Health and Social Security, entitled *The Way Forward*.

The Way Forward[1] was a brave title for Mr. David Ennals, Secretary of State for Health and Social Security, to choose for still another document on priorities in the National Health Service recently published by his department. In the introduction he points out that this new document should be regarded as complementary to the Consultative Document[2] published by his predecessor, Mrs. Barbara Castle, in 1976, and he claims that it has been written in the light of comments received in response to this Consultative Document and also in response to reactions to the controversial report of the working party on the reallocation of resources, known as RAWP.[3] Both documents were widely criticized, and Mrs. Castle had undertaken to modify the proposals in the light of comments received from health authorities, professional bodies and the community health councils representing consumer interest. Mrs. Castle's document on priorities was criticized because it was thought that it overemphasized the need to improve the community services and the services for the elderly, the young, the mentally ill and the handicapped at the expense of the acute-hospital sector, in which expansion was to be restrained and even existing facilities curtailed. The RAWP report was criticized not because there was any dispute about the need to allocate resources throughout the country so that patients would receive adequate treatment no matter where they might live, but because the proposed method of reallocating funds on a formula based on population numbers and morbidity would be a threat to centers of excellence, particularly in London and the southeast, where there are large numbers of undergraduate teaching hospitals and postgraduate institutes. Defending such centers of excellence, the *British Medical Journal*[4] pointed out that many have taken generations to establish, and although they are expensive to maintain, their influence on the upholding of standards and the advancement of medicine extends far beyond the immediate boundaries of the areas that they serve. For these reasons urgent representations were made to the Department of Health and Social Security to modify its proposals, which if rigidly implemented could have a disastrous effect on the best of British medicine.

But as the *British Medical Journal*[5] points out in commenting on Mr. Ennals' new document, there is no evidence that the Department has listened to its critics, and there seems to be almost no modification of the original proposals either on priorities or on the reallocation of resources, apart from those dictated by the serious economic state of the country. Indeed, Mr. Ennals' document makes depressing reading, particularly for consultants concerned with the care of patients in hospitals for the acutely ill. Throughout, there is a clear dedication to the principle of egalitarianism, with emphasis on the need to achieve a national pattern by redistribution of resources. And there is a warning that public expectations of health and social services will frequently outrun supply, so that hard decisions will be needed to hold back some services to allow others to develop. Mr. Ennals admits in particular that a policy of restricting the growth of the acute-hospital services has been adopted quite deliberately with a full awareness of the consequences. Thus, he warns that in some districts, long sought improvements will be further delayed and some hospitals will have to continue to manage with facilities that are outdated or inadequate. He states that he appreciates that the expectations both of the professions and of the users will not be fully satisfied, but regards this as the price that has to be paid if progress is to be made in the parts of the service that have been given priority for development. He points out that the number of hospital beds has been reduced by 4.6 per cent since 1970, and the average length of stay from 11.3 to 10.2 days. He regards this decrease as evidence of increased efficiency, but states that further restraint on the acute sector is necessary — and this development will require increased rationalization, with the closing of hospitals in some places and the curtailment of services in others. He admits that health authorities, professional bodies and individual doctors have warned of the frustration that they will feel at this continuing delay in achieving their long unfulfilled expectations, and they have expressed their anxiety that patients will suffer from these shortcomings in the service. But Mr. Ennals believes that the extent of such shortcomings can be reduced if there is a vigorous pursuit of efficiency and economy, an identification of priorities within the acute sector and a willingness, particularly among those in the medical profession, to accept this policy and to join in planning it.

Such an exhortation is unlikely to arouse much enthusiasm

among hospital consultants, whose morale is already at a low ebb, and who find great difficulty in identifying anything forward-looking in Mr. Ennals' document. No one would dispute the need to provide good medical care throughout the country so long as it is done on the principle of upgrading inadequate facilities without detriment to services elsewhere. But the implementation of the RAWP policy of redistributing budgets in a period of high inflation has already had unfortunate results. Thus, the standards in donor regions have inevitably fallen because of their reduced budgets, but the standards in many receptor regions have not been raised because their increased budgets have only just enabled them to keep pace with inflation.

On the question of closing of hospitals, the medical newspaper *On Call*[6] agrees that Mr. Ennals is right to point out that old hospitals should be closed when new ones have been built to replace them. But he does not mention the fact that some health authorities have been unable to open wards in new hospitals because of lack of funds, whereas other health authorities have had to close hospitals that had not outlived their usefulness. Thus, in the Oxford Health Region, which suffered a budgetary cut, beds had to be closed in the Spinal Injuries Unit at Stoke Mandeville, which has a worldwide reputation as a center of excellence; it has not been possible to open a new intensive-therapy unit in the same hospital, nor will it be possible to open all the new wards recently completed at the John Radcliffe Hospital in Oxford unless more funds become available.

Mr. Ennals has claimed that nearly all hospital closings have been part of rationalization plans and not due to financial stringency, but an independent investigation by *The Sunday Times*[7] revealed that in fact 50 per cent of all closures were due to lack of funds. And as these closures proceed in the public sector, the Health Services Board, established to separate private practice from the National Health Service, has announced a date for the closure of a further batch of private beds. But as the *Daily Telegraph*[8] pointed out in an editorial, the withdrawal of these beds is likely to lead not to the provision of any extra public beds but simply to vacant space and underemployed services in hospitals, in addition to the loss of considerable revenue to the health service. The *Daily Telegraph* sees no possible justification for such leveling down and concludes that standards in the health service will inevitably fall because the individual as a taxpayer will not provide funds to do for society as a whole what he would do for himself and his dependents, possibly at greater personal sacrifice. The editorial suggests that faced with this truth, a wise government would be considering means of harnessing once again, for the support of medicine, the elementary human instincts that sustained it in the past.

Such a possibility, of course, has been considered by the Conservative Party — at present in opposition, and hoping for a return to power after the next general election. But, as the *Lancet*[9] points out, it may be very difficult for a new Conservative government to make radical changes either in the administration or in the financial basis of the health service. From a study of the possibility of introducing new health charges it seems that this issue has been set aside, at least until after the election, because many Conservatives believe that the Labour Party and the unions would make political capital out of any such suggestion. On the other hand, the *Lancet* thinks that the Conservatives really do consider the National Health Service to be in a shambles, with no strong leadership and a lack of decision making at every level. At the top they see the government waiting for the Royal Commission on the National Health Service to make its report, and at the bottom they see an inability to get anything decided quickly, whether it concerns the action required to have a piece of equipment repaired, a new unit opened or a staff vacancy filled. The Conservatives believe, therefore, that more decision making should be possible at the local level, and that the area health authorities, introduced when the Service was reorganized in 1974, might be eliminated. The *Lancet* believes that the Conservatives, like the present government, incline to the view that misuse of funds may be a greater problem than underfunding of the health service. But they would encourage rather than discourage the growth of the private sector in the belief that any money spent privately on health must be of benefit to the public sector; it is expected that the Conservative Party will soon publish a policy document on its attitude to the future development of the National Health Service. It must be hoped that it will have a more distinctive forward look than Mr. Ennals' document, which if anything seems to incline backward.

Meanwhile, there are many patients in need of treatment. It was timely that Sir Douglas Black, president of the Royal College of Physicians of London, should have selected "Cui Bono?" as the title for his Harveian oration. He reflected on the fact that criticism of doctors is no new thing and recalled that the Puritan levelers had been unfriendly to all the professions. More recently, doctors had been criticized not only by patients but also by politicians and sometimes by medical sociologists. But Sir Douglas thought that it should be realized that most doctors actually like their patients to get better, and he emphasized the need for all concerned to remember that the practice of medicine is primarily for the benefit of patients. He did not think that economic accountability and clinical excellence should be incompatible, but he recognized that heightened expectations and increased demands by patients have put strains on the present medical system, which is inappropriate for meeting demands that have previously been met by family, church and school. He agreed that doctors should be educated in the proper and most effective use of resources and should understand the economic cost of their actions and make balanced decisions in the light of existing constraints. Recalling that William Harvey, in his day, had encouraged the Fellows of the Royal College of Physicians to discover the secrets of medicine by reorienting their outlook from that of humanistic Galenism to the discipline of experimental physiology, Sir Douglas suggested that the need today is for doctors to develop a more altruistic outlook and to acknowledge once again a duty to set the needs of patients above their own self-interest. No practicing physician could challenge such a philosophy, but it has to be said that the attitude of present-day politicians, who seem to be as unfriendly to the professions as the early levelers, does not make altruism a virtue that is easy to cultivate.

It is understood that the ruling politicians are now concerned about the low state of morale in the medical profession, especially among hospital consultants, and they are anxious to know how to improve it. They must know that they could do so quite easily, but the price would be too high, for it would involve changing their whole attitude both to the health service and to the medical profession, and their dedication to the principle of egalitarianism will not allow them to do so. Nevertheless, until standards of excellence and individual initiative are encouraged rather than discouraged, the Health Service will continue to incline backward rather than look forward.

---

1. The way forward: priorities in the health and social services. London: Her Majesty's Stationery Office, 1977.

2. Priorities for health and personal social services in England: a consultative document. London: Her Majesty's Stationery Office, 1976.

3. Sharing resources for health in England — report of the Resource Allocation Working Party. London: Her Majesty's Stationery Office, 1976.

4. The end of excellence? Br Med J 1976; 2:779-780.

5. Obdurate politics. Br Med J 1977; 2:785-786.

6. Exploding myths. On Call, October 13, 1977.

7. The truth about hospital cuts. The Sunday Times, October 16, 1977.

8. Rationing health. Daily Telegraph, October 17, 1977.

9. Conservative caution on N.H.S. Lancet 1977; 2:882-883.

🜋 *Drifting off Course*

Mr. David Ennals was Secretary of State at the Department of Health and Social Security when the National Health Service celebrated its 30th anniversary in 1978. He had hoped to summarize its achievements in a statement agreed to by medical and nursing organizations and by the health-service unions. However, he was unable to obtain agreement on what he should say — particularly in relation to the participation of NHS staff in industrial action. It had been hoped that such action would be outlawed, but with so many interests involved it was not possible to obtain a consensus. Unfortunately, there were many other problems at the time, and there was a distinct impression that the NHS was indeed drifting off course.

The National Health Service (NHS) celebrated its 30th anniversary on July 5 with an official government luncheon over which the Prime Minister presided.

The Secretary of State for Social Services, Mr. David Ennals, had hoped to be able to mark the occasion with the publication of a joint statement about the past achievements of the service and its prospects for the future that had been agreed on not only by all the major medical and nursing organizations but also by the health-service trade unions. A vital part of this statement would have been a declaration of intent to outlaw industrial action in hospitals when it might prove harmful to patients. With so many interests involved it is not surprising

164

that agreement could not be reached on the wording of such a statement, however widely the sentiment might be applauded.

Clearly, no one would wish to gainsay the achievements of the NHS, and no one practicing medicine could fail to accept the major principle on which it was founded: that no patient should be denied necessary treatment because of a financial barrier. But one must nevertheless admit that 30 years after its inception, the NHS has drifted badly off course. As the *British Medical Journal*[1] points out, it now measures poorly against many alternative methods of providing health care, and its medical and nursing staff are disillusioned and depressed.

It is therefore more appropriate that this 30th anniversary should be made the occasion for an objective look at the state of the service rather than for indulgence in a self-congratulatory exercise. And such an assessment is what Sir Francis Avery Jones has made in a perceptive paper in the *British Medical Journal*[2] identifying the major factors that have led to the deterioration of the NHS, particularly in the hospitals, and suggesting measures that might set it back on course.

He believes that the combined effect of the complex administrative reorganization of the health service that took place in 1974 and the political attack on private practice that reached a climax shortly afterwards had a disastrous effect on the morale of hospital consultants. Thus, although the reorganization provided for the participation of a small number of practicing doctors in management, it greatly weakened the medical advisory machinery that previously existed, and made it far more difficult for experienced clinicians to influence the decisions of hospital authorities. The attack on private practice was seen as a threat to professional freedom, and the publication of a series of documents by the Department of Health on the reallocation of resources,[3] the identification of priorities[4] and forward planning,[5] all written by economists, civil servants and administrators with no recent clinical contact, simply compounded the confusion and sense of frustration felt by senior consultants. Sir

Francis thought it was not surprising that, having struggled in vain to overcome the system, many of them eventually stopped trying to expand their clinical activity and concentrated on developing their own personal interests. Meanwhile, the losers must inevitably be the patients, and Sir Francis urges all concerned to remember that the NHS is there for patients who come to be treated and not to be administered.

At present a Royal Commission is investigating the problems of the health service, and it is hoped that it will report next year. The Commission has in fact just published the report[6] of a research team set up to investigate the allegation that the present structure of the NHS leads to delays in getting decisions made and consequently to frustration and inefficiency. Having interviewed 500 health-service employees, the team concluded that the structure is indeed top-heavy, with too many levels of administration and too much duplication of functions.

The team also criticized the complex process of consultation required in the reorganized service, pointing out that the need to consult so many people on so many issues creates extra work and delays decision making. This view would certainly be that of most clinicians, but Professor Rudolf Klein[7] points out that, in many respects, these problems of the NHS are a reflection of the problems that British society has created for itself by demanding that scarce resources should be fairly shared, that those working in national organizations should participate in decision making and that the views of the consumers should be sought and considered.

The problems created by the effort to reconcile these conflicting demands are not peculiar to the NHS. Indeed, analogies could be drawn from experience in other nationalized industries. Professor Klein claims that the medical profession in Britain, right from the time that the first health-insurance scheme was introduced in 1911, insisted on participation in policy making. Following the lead of the doctors, other professional groups and trades unions involved in health care are demanding a similar right. Thus, the diffusion of power has become a reality, but the assignment of responsibility for the consequences of the exercise of that power remains to be achieved; Klein believes that this may be the major task for the NHS over the next 30 years. He also thinks that there should be a clearer definition of accountability and believes that if it were possible to develop clinically accountable teams responsible for their own budgets, the flexibility of the health service could be increased and local needs better met.

However, these developments are for the long term, but there is clearly an urgent need to restore morale in the hospital service. Sir Francis Avery Jones believes that the immediate requirements are good leadership, some simplification of the administrative structure and the reinstatement of the lay public in the management of district hospitals. The proposed new consultant contract, although not acceptable to all, has been approved in principle by a majority of those who returned their ballot papers. Final acceptance is subject to satisfactory pricing by the Review Body, but if this goal is obtained, it might open the way for a return to the spirit of co-operation between the medical profession and those administering the NHS that contributed so greatly to its earlier success. If the NHS is ever to become a first-rate service again, however, the politicians will also have to change their attitude toward it. The present administration is not only obsessed with following egalitarian principles but is totally opposed to considering any change in the method of financing the service — and apparently not prepared to deviate from its policy of reallocating resources. Certainly, there are deprived areas of the country that require additional funds, but it is a short-sighted solution to attempt to provide them by reallocating funds from London and the southeast, where there is a concentration of internationally known teaching hospitals and postgraduate institutes that are inevitably expensive to maintain. Unless research is encouraged and unless these centers of excellence and teaching are supported and recognized as the institutions that set the standards for the rest of the service, the present drift toward uniformity and mediocrity is bound to continue.

1. The disalienation of the NHS. Br Med J 1978; 2:1-2.
2. Jones FA. Getting the NHS back on course. Br Med J 1978; 2:5-9.
3. Sharing resources for health in England: report of the Resource Allocation Working Party. London: Her Majesty's Stationery Office, 1976.
4. Priorities for health and personal social services in England: a consultative document. London: Her Majesty's Stationery Office, 1976.
5. The way forward: priorities in the health and social services. London: Her Majesty's Stationery Office, 1977.
6. The working of the National Health Service (research paper no. 1). London: Her Majesty's Stationery Office, 1978.
7. Klein R. Who decides?: patterns of authority. Br Med J 1978; 2:73-74.

Thirty Years On

Mr. Enoch Powell, a former Minister of Health, celebrated the 30th anniversary of the National Health Service by reporting a dialogue with an American friend in which they considered how British medicine might have developed during the previous three decades if the NHS had never been introduced.

Mr. Enoch Powell may be remembered for having pointed out in his book on medicine and politics[1] that, because the demand for medical care is infinite but resources are finite, some form of rationing is inevitable. Or he may be remembered for having remarked that ministers of health soon learn that money is the only topic that they ever discuss with the doctors.

In recent years he has had less to say on medical matters, and it was with some interest that I read his contribution to the *Spectator*[2] at the time of the 30th anniversary of the inception of the National Health Service (NHS) last July. This message took the form of the report of a dialogue with an American friend who had asked him how different British medicine would have been if there had been no NHS. The American was apparently horrified when Mr. Powell told him that it would have been barely different at all. Mr. Powell then explained to him that over the last 30 years, the proportion of the national income that Britain has devoted to health care has been similar to that of other European countries, though not so high as in the United States. On the other hand, the health-care delivery system in these other countries has been quite different from the NHS, and Mr. Powell could see little reason to suppose that if the system in Britain had been different, the effort devoted to medical care would have been any less.

His American friend was still unconvinced, so Mr. Powell went on to explain that when the NHS was introduced, it absorbed three distinct systems. One was the municipal hospital service, which provided care at minimal or no cost to the patient, the second was insurance, which covered a great part of the population, and the third comprised various charitable bodies. Mr. Powell believed that if there had been no NHS, all three channels would have expanded during the last 30 years under the influence of increasing affluence and national income. Mr. Powell was not even impressed with his friend's suggestion that people did not get medical attention before the NHS because they could not afford to pay for it. In the past, general practitioners related their charges to their patients' ability to pay and considered it in the honor of their profession to refuse no one treatment. Mr. Powell also pointed out that because a government health service is nominally managed by the politicians, it is assumed that these politicians have powers of control far greater than they actually possess.

Thus, the pattern of medical facilities that Aneurin Bevan took over in 1948 was the product of the evolution of past generations, and he was able to alter it only minimally year by year. Furthermore, Mr. Powell went on to explain to his American friend, the innovations in medicine that have occurred in the last 30 years were not decided by politicians, or even by the medical profession, but have been the consequences of forces working in medicine and society that were beyond the foresight of those responsible for running the NHS, either political or professional. Indeed, Mr. Powell believed that the world, including the NHS, is very much what it is bound to be. And if obliged to identify some differences that nationalization of health care has made, he would say that it has added a psychologic dimension. Thus, the inevitable and the automatic have been invested with the fallacious appearance of being intentional and avoidable. Furthermore, once the state takes responsibility for a service there is always someone to blame for its shortcomings — the politicians. And so, as Mr. Powell recalled he once said himself, continual complaint and perpetual dissatisfaction is the enduring atmosphere of the NHS.

I must admit that I found this a somewhat cynical anniversary message for a previous health minister to be offering. But, of course, whenever Mr. Powell intervenes in a debate he can always be counted upon to be original, provocative and stimulating, and on reflection there is no doubt that there is a good deal of truth in what he had to say.

1. Powell JE. A new look at medicine and politics. London: Pitman Medical, 1978.
2. *Idem*. Thirty years of the NHS. Spectator, July 8, 1978.

New Ministers and New Ideas

JULY 26, 1979

The general election in May 1979 brought about a change in government that was to have a profound effect on the National Health Service. Apart from the four years of the Heath government there had been a Labour administration since 1964, and during those years the NHS had become progressively more socialized. The new Conservative government had a totally different philosophy. It professed to believe in the Health Service and hoped that it would prosper. On the other hand, it believed strongly in all forms of private enterprise and encouraged the growth of the private sector in medicine. It was hoped that a partnership between the public and private sectors would develop that would be beneficial to both parties. Labour politicians were skeptical. The extent to which this hope has been fulfilled has probably disappointed the Conservatives.

As anticipated, when Mrs. Margaret Thatcher formed her new government, she appointed Mr. Patrick Jenkin to be Secretary of State in the Department of Health and Social Security (DHSS), with Dr. Gerard Vaughan as Minister of Health. During the last few years, both men have acted as opposition spokesmen on matters relating to health and social security, and they therefore assume office with wide experience concerning the problems of the National Health Service (NHS); Dr. Vaughan has the additional advantage of having been a practicing psychiatrist. They are both committed to upholding the principles of the NHS, but they made it clear in Parliament and during the election campaign that they believe that some changes are necessary and that efforts should be made to resolve the long-standing disputes about the place of private practice both inside and outside the NHS.

In his book on *Medicine and Politics*,[1] Mr. Enoch Powell remarked that the unnerving discovery that every new Minister of Health makes is that the only subject he is destined to discuss with the doctors is money, whether for themselves, their staff or their departmental requirements. Mr. Jenkin and Dr. Vaughan were well aware that one of their first tasks would be to talk to the doctors about money, because when they took over at the DHSS, they found the latest report of the Review Body on Doctors' and Dentists' Pay awaiting their attention. Publication of this report was withheld by the previous Prime Minister, Mr. James Callaghan, because the size of the pay increases recommended would have been embarrassing at the time of the election. Many public-service workers had been granted increases of about 9 per cent, but to implement the final phase of a previous award and to update the rates of pay for the current year, the total increase recommended for doctors was expected to be nearly 30 per cent. This projected increase was unfortunate for a new government with a declared aim to control and reduce public spending, but the negotiators for the profession had made it clear that they would be expecting the government to implement the recommendations fully, and it was thought that the government would be equally anxious to make a generous award to help restore the morale of the doctors and thus create a new spirit of co-operation between the administration and the profession. No doubt Mr. Jenkin had to argue the doctors' case with his cabinet colleagues, but present indications are that an increase of about 20 per cent will be offered immediately, with the balance being deferred until next year.

In a speech at a dinner given by the British Medical Association, Mr. Jenkin gave some indication of his thoughts for the future.[2] He said that he would prefer to see the NHS as a series of local health services, providing care on a community basis and managed by persons in each community, rather than as the giant centralized system that it has become. He thought that some of the industrial problems that beset the NHS last winter might have been avoided if local managers had more authority. He also emphasized the importance of ending the vendetta between the NHS and the private sector of medical care, but he was not specific about his proposals in this field. Nevertheless, it is anticipated that the role of the Health Services Board, which was set up by the Labour government to phase out private beds in NHS hospitals and control the building of new private hospitals, may be modified to enable it to promote a partnership between the NHS and the private sector. Thus, the *Lancet*[3] suggests that the government is keen to develop joint schemes between the private and the public sectors in which the private sector would offer preventive and diagnostic services to the NHS on an agency basis. It is also thought that the phasing out of pay-beds from the NHS hospitals will be halted so long as there is a demand for them, and it is expected that legislation will be introduced that would allow hospitals with pay-beds to keep the revenue they receive from their use. At present, this revenue has to be returned to central funds, and it is hoped that by allowing hospitals to keep the money the unpopularity of private beds among many NHS staff would be reduced, particularly if it were shown that the additional funds were being used to improve services for both patients and staff. There will undoubtedly be opposition to proposals for a renewed partnership (especially from the health-service unions, which have already threatened industrial action), but many will welcome these refreshing ideas, which should help to restore the incentive and enthusiasm within the NHS that have been so sadly lacking during recent years.

1. Powell JE. Medicine and politics. London: Pitman Medical Publishing, 1966.
2. Jenkin pledges to streamline N.H.S. The Guardian, May 31, 1979.
3. Help for the N.H.S. from the private sector. Lancet 1979; 1:1151.

General Medical Council

Ever since the General Medical Council was established in 1858 it has been the regulator of the medical profession, protecting the public by maintaining a register of duly qualified practitioners, setting standards for undergraduate education, and acting as the disciplinary body for the profession. The Council has always been regarded as a professional body, but although some members have always been elected, before the new Medical Act of 1978 they were outnumbered by members from universities, colleges, and government. The Act of 1978 provided for a much larger council with a majority of elected members. The Council was also made responsible for supervising postgraduate as well as undergraduate training. The implications of these changes are considered in this Post.

The General Medical Council was established by the Medical Act of 1858, and since that time it has functioned as the regulator of the medical profession in the United Kingdom and Ireland. The Act of 1858 was passed largely as the result of initiative within the profession — the establishment of the Council was desired as much for the protection of the duly qualified medical practitioner from the competition of unqualified practitioners as for the protection of the public. Thus, the Act stated that "it is expedient that persons requiring medical aid should be able to distinguish qualified from unqualified practitioners," and all of the Council's activities have evolved from that original objective. Over the years, the boundaries of medical science have enlarged, and the task has become more complicated, but the Council has fulfilled its original duty of protecting the public by keeping and publishing a register of duly qualified doctors, by ensuring that the educational standard of entry to the register is maintained and by taking disciplinary action against registered doctors if it appears, by reason of misconduct, that they should not remain on the register.

Some modifications in the responsibilities of the Council have occurred as the result of further medical acts; in particular, the Medical Act of 1950 made it mandatory for every newly graduated doctor to spend a year in resident house-officer posts before becoming fully registered. There have, however, been no radical changes either in the composition or in the activities of the Council for many years. In 1972, Sir Keith Joseph, then Secretary of State in the Department of Health and Social Security, decided to set up an independent committee of inquiry to consider what changes were needed in the existing provisions for the regulation of the medical profession, what functions should be assigned to the body charged with the responsibility for its regulation and how the body should be constituted. Dr. A.W. (now Sir Alec) Merrison, vice-chancellor of Bristol University, was appointed chairman and presented his report[1] to the government in 1975. Important changes were recommended, many of which were embodied in a new Medical Act of 1978; in the Annual Report of the Council, its president, Lord Richardson, has outlined the changes that will take place later this year.[2]

One of the major changes relates to the composition of the Council, which will be greatly enlarged, with a new total membership of 95, of which 50 persons will be elected by the profession, so that elected members will be in the majority (at present, they are well in the minority, comprising only 11 of the present much smaller total of 47 members). In the new Council, 34 members will be appointed by the Royal Colleges or Faculties; the remaining 11 members, mostly laymen, will be appointed by the Privy Council. The election will be conducted by postal vote, and the reconstituted Council will take office on September 27, 1979, which has been designated Succession Day. Lord Richardson points out that ever since the Council was established in 1858, members from southern Ireland and doctors graduating there have been registered on the same basis as those graduating in other parts of the British Isles. These arrangements survived the partition of Ireland in 1921, but sadly the new Council will contain no members from the Irish Republic, although it is hoped that a liaison will be maintained between the education committees of the new Council and the Medical Council of Ireland. In the field of medical education, the new Council will have an expanded role. Whereas previously the Council's functions have legally been largely restricted to maintaining minimum standards of undergraduate medical education, the education committee of the new Council will be given the general function of promoting high standards of medical education and coordinating all stages of medical education, thus extending its influence into the postgraduate field.

The other important area in which the General Medical Council is given new responsibilities is in relation to the sick doctor. Great concern was expressed in the Merrison Report that the Council did not have any power to control the right of sick doctors to practice. The Medical Act of 1978 has therefore provided for the new Council to establish a committee to consider cases in which a doctor's fitness to practice is seriously impaired. In addition to these responsibilities, the Council will also be expected to complement its present disciplinary function by advising members of the medical profession on standards of professional conduct or on medical ethics.

The old Council has served both the profession and the public well, and the new one, with its expanded membership and updated role, will doubtless do so, too.

1. Report of the Committee of Inquiry into the Regulation of the Medical Profession. London: Her Majesty's Stationery Office, 1975.
2. General Medical Council — Annual Report for 1978. London: Office of the General Medical Council, 1978.

The Royal Commission Reports

The Royal Commission on the National Health Service, which was appointed in 1976, undertook the first major review of the objectives, the achievements, and the failures of the Service. The Commission was appointed by a Labour government at a time when there was great unrest in the NHS, and it finally reported in 1979 to a Conservative government with a markedly different view of the way in which the Health Service should function. The fact that few of the recommendations have been implemented is not surprising, because this appears to be the fate of most recommendations of Royal Commissions. Nevertheless, the report did stimulate a debate on many important aspects of the NHS, including the best way of funding it. The Commission was uncertain about how to advise on this, except to express the view that there seemed little advantage in changing from a system largely funded from direct taxation to one based on insurance. It also recommended that eventually all charges should be withdrawn so that the Service would be genuinely free at the time of use. In fact, the new Conservative government has been unable to afford to withdraw any existing charges and has increased prescription charges steeply and would have liked to change to an insurance-based funding system. However, this latter proposal has now been discarded because of both political and practical considerations. But even though few of the recommendations of the Commission have been implemented, the report itself remains a useful source of information about many aspects of health care.

The Report of the Royal Commission on the National Health Service[1] (NHS), set up in 1976 under the chairmanship of Sir Alec Merrison, Vice-Chancellor of Bristol University, was published in July. The full report is lengthy, but the recommendations have been summarized in both the *Lancet*[2] and the *British Medical Journal*.[3]

In the opening chapter of the report it is recalled that the Commission was set up at a time when there was widespread concern about the future of the NHS. It had been disturbed by the reorganization of 1974, and it was suffering from the effects of a series of industrial disputes, some of which related to the decision of the Labour government to phase out private beds from the NHS. It was also suffering from the adverse economic situations of the mid-1970's. The commissioners were "To consider in the interests both of the patients and those who work in the National Health Service the best use and management of the financial and manpower resources of the National Health Service."

The commissioners set about their task by inviting suggestions from the public on the problems of the NHS that they should examine, and in the light of more than 1000 replies they published a list of topics as a guide to those submitting evidence. In their subsequent work they received written evidence from 2460 individuals or organizations, they held 58 hearings, and they spoke to about 2800 people during the course of visits within the United Kingdom and abroad.

In sifting their evidence and forming their opinions the commissioners were guided by what they believed the objectives of the NHS should be, and they declared their belief that it should encourage and assist individuals to remain healthy; provide equality of entitlement to health services; provide a broad range of services of a high standard; provide equality of access to these services; provide a service free at the time of use; satisfy the reasonable expectations of its users; and remain a national service responsive to local needs.

They were aware that some of these objectives are controversial and others unattainable, but they tried to determine how nearly the NHS was meeting those objectives, by studying its record of service to its consumers — the patients. A survey that they commissioned indicated that 80 per cent of inpatients thought that the service they received was good or very good, and a primary-care survey indicated that on the whole the NHS did provide an accessible service, generally appreciated by its users.

On the other hand, health workers were critical of the NHS, and although the commissioners recognized that they were in the best position to see defects in the service, they thought that health-service workers tended to take too gloomy a view of the NHS. At the same time they recognized that the morale of the medical profession had been adversely affected by the erosion of their status and influence that took place in recent years when their authority was challenged by the rising influence of other professions. They were also aware of the criticism that the reorganized NHS contained one unnecessary tier of administration, with consequent delays in decision making, and that there were too many administrators and too little money for the efficient running of the service.

It was against this background that the Commission deliberated and finally reached its conclusions and made its recommendations. In his introduction to a short booklet[4] that summarized these recommendations, Sir Alec Merrison states that he and his colleagues found much to praise, not a little to criticize and much to recommend during their three-year study of the NHS.

The Commission quite properly studied the NHS as a service for patients and tried to determine how it was performing in that role, but there has been some disappointment among those providing the service that the basic problem of funding the enterprise was not tackled more robustly. Indeed, the questions of management and finance were relegated to the last section of the report, with the comment that they are essentially secondary to those subjects with a direct bearing on patient care. This seems a remarkably naive attitude, particularly in view of the fact that concern about the adverse effects of administrative and financial difficulties on patient care was one of the major reasons for appointing the Commission.

However, the main conclusions of the Commission on finance were that there is no universally acceptable method of establishing the right level of expenditure on the NHS, that the nation should spend more on the NHS as it becomes wealthier, and that there is no method of financing a part of national expenditure as large and as politically sensitive as the health service that would be likely to remove it from government influence. Nor was the Commission convinced that any advantages of insurance financing or substantial increase in revenue charges would outweigh their disadvantages in terms of equity and administrative cost. But, having reached these conclusions, the Commission appeared to evade the issue of how the service should be financed, stating that it is for the government to decide this matter. At the same time it recommended that eventually all charges should be withdrawn.

As anticipated, the Commission accepted the view that reorganization had introduced one administrative tier too many and, although not specifically mentioning the elimination of area health authorities, it did recommend that except in a minority of cases, there should be only one tier below the regional health authorities (or below the health departments in the case of Northern Ireland, Scotland and Wales). It also recommended that regional health authorities rather than the central health departments should become accountable to Parliament for matters within their competence. These would include most of the activities of the NHS apart from apportioning revenue and capital funds between regions, which would have to be undertaken centrally.

Furthermore, it was suggested that the number and the roles of administrators at various levels should be reviewed in the light of the criticism that the Commission had received about expensive, slow and cumbersome decision making. This had been well expressed by one hospital medical committee, which said, "The proliferation of committees and the introduction of democracy has meant unlimited opportunities for extremists to manipulate the system for their own ends and for postponement of decisions to faceless committees at higher levels."

On the issue of private practice, the Commission concluded that the private sector is too small to have an impact on the NHS except locally and temporarily. On the other hand, it conceded that the private sector responds much more directly to patients' demands for services than the NHS and that it provides a useful pointer to areas where the NHS is deficient. Thus, half the abortions carried out on residents of the United Kingdom are undertaken privately, many elderly patients are accommodated in private nursing homes, and patients awaiting elective surgery often seek private treatment. Reviewing the work of the Health Services Board set up in 1976 by the Labour government to phase out pay-beds from NHS hospitals, the Commission noted that the number of such beds had fallen from 4859 in 1976 to 2968 in 1979. At the same time there had been an increase in the number of beds in private hospitals and nursing homes, the total number of such beds in 1977 being nearly 35,000. After considering the evidence for and against private practice in NHS hospitals the Commission concluded that the presence or absence of pay-beds in NHS hospitals is not important from the standpoint of the efficient functioning of the NHS. On the other hand, it recognized that the main importance of pay-beds lies in the passions aroused and the dislocation of work that follows. The establishment of the Health Services Board had led to a welcome respite from discussions of this emotional subject, but to carry out its function of safeguarding the interests of the NHS the Commission recommended that the board should be given power to control not only private beds in NHS hospitals but the aggregate of beds in all private hospitals and nursing homes in any locality where new development is being considered.

In its report the Commission had much to say about priorities and about the need for more emphasis on preventive medicine. It pointed out that more than 60 per cent of NHS expenditure is already devoted to the care of the young, the elderly and the mentally and physically handicapped. Responsibility for the care of these groups falls largely on general practitioners and the community services, and the development of group practices and health centers with adequate nursing and ancillary staff has been justified. On the other hand, the Commission found evidence of a need for more research into certain aspects of the community services and primary care where standards are variable. Thus, concern was expressed about the cost of drugs, dressings and appliances prescribed by general practitioners. In the year 1977–78 this amounted to £539.5 million, the bulk of which was spent on drugs. The cost of all other prescriptions was about £127 million, most of which was incurred in hospitals. It was recognized that general practitioners are under pressure to prescribe both from patients and the pharmaceutical industry, but it was suggested that some economy might be achieved if the health departments introduced a limited list of drugs prescribable through the NHS. It was also recommended that more general practitioners should introduce methods to audit the services that they provide. And to remedy the inadequate primary-care services in inner-city areas it was suggested that when health centers are established in such areas, they should offer salaried appointments and reduced list sizes to attract doctors to work in them. This would clearly be a controversial proposal since general practitioners have always regarded their self-employed status as vital in protecting their professional freedom.

The importance of preventive medicine is emphasized with the positive recommendation that the wearing of seat belts should be made compulsory for drivers and front-seat passengers in motor vehicles, and in the chapter on dentistry the government is urged to introduce legislation on fluoridation. It was also recommended that the budget of the Health Education Council should be increased so that all aspects of health education could be expanded.

In a chapter on the role of doctors, the question of medical manpower was considered. The Commission had received evidence from the Hospital Junior Staff Committee of the British Medical Association suggesting that unless student numbers were cut there would be medical unemployment in the foreseeable future. But evidence from the health departments did not support this view, and the Commission concluded that the planned intake of about 4000 students each year would be unlikely to lead to medical unemployment during this century. At the same time it was recognized that the geographic distribution of doctors and the distribution within specialties are unsatisfactory, and it may be that future doctors will not have the choice of specialty and place of practice that they have at present. Indeed, it was suggested that the health departments should show more determination in enforcing their priorities in the specialties in short supply, if necessary by blocking expansion of other specialties, and should be more critically involved in the development of new specialties. Whether such a policy of negative direction of labor would solve the manpower problem of unpopular specialties must be open to considerable doubt. Nevertheless, there is general agreement that the career structure in the hospital service is unsatisfactory, with too many doctors in training posts and too few in career posts, and the

Commission has proposed a revised career structure that includes a new intermediate grade described as "physician," which would be both a training and a career grade. Many of these physicians would graduate to consultant status, but some would remain in the grade, carrying clinical responsibility matched to the individual's ability and seniority in the grade. The proposal is ingenious but unlikely to find favor with the British Medical Association, which has always refused to recognize any subconsultant grade.

Many other aspects of the NHS are covered in the report, which is a mine of useful information. Indeed, as the *Lancet*[5] points out, Sir Alec Merrison and his colleagues have carried out the first comprehensive survey of the NHS since it began, and although they admit that they have been unable to emerge with any blinding revelation that would transform all deficiencies into perfection, they believe that if their recommendations are accepted the NHS will become more suited for the health of the nation.

But of course it was a Labour administration that appointed the Commission, and a Conservative one that has received the report and must decide how to handle the recommendations. Some of them are clearly not consistent with Conservative policy on health. In particular, the recommendation to phase out all charges is awkward for a government that has just announced an increase in prescription charges, and the recommendation that further powers be given to the Health Services Board presents a problem since the government has already announced its intention of disbanding it. The refusal of the Commission to consider alternative methods of financing the service is also unhelpful to an administration that has indicated that sources of finance other than direct taxation may be sought.

Other aspects of the report will be more acceptable to Mr. Patrick Jenkin, Secretary of State at the Department of Health, who will welcome the advised devolution in management and accountability, including the removal of one tier of administration. In any case he will doubtless receive advice from many quarters on how he and the government should react to the report, and he has promised to make a major statement on Conservative plans for the NHS when Parliament reassembles in the autumn.

1. Report of the Royal Commission on the National Health Service. London: Her Majesty's Stationery Office, 1979.
2. Royal Commission on the N.H.S. Lancet 1979; 2:142-143.
3. The Royal Commission on the N.H.S. Br Med J 1979; 2:284.
4. A service for patients: conclusions and recommendations of the Royal Commission's Report. London: Her Majesty's Stationery Office, 1979.
5. The Royal Commission. Lancet 1979; 2:181-183.

Patients First

The initial response of the Conservative Government to the report of the Royal Commission was to publish a consultative paper entitled *Patients First*. This paper emphasized that the primary objective of the National Health Service is to meet the needs of patients, and that doctors and nurses require good administrative support to enable them to serve patients. A simplified administrative structure was therefore proposed, with the elimination of one tier of the administration and the delegation of more responsibility to local Districts.

The government has responded to the report of the Royal Commission on the National Health Service (NHS)[1] by publishing a paper[2] summarizing its proposals for changes in the structure and management of the NHS in England and Wales. This document, with the imaginative title *Patients First*, is commendably brief, and, as the title indicates, the emphasis is on identifying the changes required to improve the standard of patient care. Thus, it is emphasized that the NHS exists to serve patients and the main objective of the government is to establish a structure that will allow efficient planning and management of the health services and within which decisions can be made by those who are most responsive to the needs of patients.

Although the 1974 reorganization achieved the objective of integrating services for patients in the hospitals and in the community, there has been widespread criticism that it created too many administrative tiers, with too many administrators. Thus, in England there are 14 Regional Health Authorities (RHA's) and 90 Area Health Authorities (AHA's), each having one or more districts. Although it was intended that there should be maximum delegation of responsibility downwards, this principle was matched by the principle of accountability upwards, and the result has been an inhibition of the decision-making process and an extremely expensive administrative machine. The Royal Commission accepted all these criticisms and defects of the present system and suggested that one administrative tier might be removed. It also suggested that the accountability of RHA's should be directly to Parliament rather than mediated through the Secretary of State at the Department of Health and Social Security (DHSS) and that local government might administer the local health services. However, the government has pointed out that the proposal regarding accountability to Parliament would be inconsistent with the statutory responsibility of the Secretary of State, and that the one involving local government would not command general support.

But the government has proposed changes that it believes would improve the present unsatisfactory situation. These changes would include the strengthening of management arrangements at the local level with greater delegation of responsibility to those in the hospitals and in the local community; in addition, the structure of the NHS would be simplified by removal of the area level of administration and establishment of District Health Authorities. The government also recognizes the need for better professional advisory machinery and for simplification of the planning system to ensure that regional plans are fully sensitive to local needs. The government shares the view of the Royal Commission that there has been a decline in the quality of hospital administration and that there is a clear need to simplify and improve the management of both the hospitals and the community services. Each District Health Authority would appoint a management team to coordinate all the health-service activities of the district, but at the same time there would be maximum delegation of authority to hospital administrators. Thus, for each major hospital or group of hospitals there should be an administrator and nurse of appropriate seniority to discharge an individual responsibility in conjunction with the medical staff.

An ideal district authority would be responsible for a locality large enough to justify the range of specialties normally found in a district general hospital, but not so large as to make members of the authority remote from the services for which they are responsible or from the staff who provide them. The population of districts would normally be between 200,000 and 500,000.

RHA's would make proposals for the restructuring of districts within their regions and in the case of districts based on teaching hospitals would consult with the universities concerned. Special arrangements would be required to maintain the links between local government and the health service in respect to their related responsibilities in the fields of child health, the school health service, social services, and environmental health.

The new District Health Authorities would have a chairman appointed by the Secretary of State and about 20 members appointed by the RHA. Each district authority would include a hospital consultant, a general practitioner, a nurse, a university nominee, and a member nominated by the trade-union movement. Local government would be adequately represented, although it was not thought necessary for local authorities to have as large a proportion of places on the new district authorities as they have on existing AHA's, where they claim one third of the membership.

The Royal Commission considered that the Community Health Councils set up as part of the 1974 reorganization to

represent consumer interest performed a useful function. However, the government points out that in the future, the members of District Health Authorities will be less remote from
local services than the members of existing AHA's, and it
questions the need for separate consumer representation, although it recognizes that consumerism is a sensitive political
issue.

Patients First also comments on the recommendations of the
Royal Commission that there should be a special inquiry into
the problems of the health services in London. That recommendation was made because of the excessive concentration of
teaching and research facilities in London and the influence of
this concentration on the provision of health services in the
capital. However, the government points out that the future
disposition of the medical and dental schools and postgraduate
institutes in London University is already being reviewed by a
special working party under the chairmanship of Lord Flow-
ers, which is due to report early this year; another inquiry
might only delay important decisions.

The government hopes that its proposals cause a minimum
of disturbance to those working in the NHS and also that
planning will not be inhibited by too much uncertainty. A
relatively brief period is therefore being allowed for consultation, and it is hoped that much of the reorganization will be
completed by mid-1982 and that all structural changes will
take effect by the end of 1983. It is estimated that when such
changes have been effected the management costs of the NHS
may be reduced by 10 per cent.

Most of the proposals in the government document should
be generally welcomed, and the *Lancet*[3] reports that Sir Alec
Merrison, the chairman of the Royal Commission, is rather
pleased with the government's approach because he believes
that it is right to start by revising the structure of the NHS. The
Labour opposition, having been highly critical of the 1974
reorganization that was introduced by the last Conservative

administration, might have been expected to welcome the proposals, but it has reacted by indicating its objection to any
reduction in local-government representation on health authorities and also its total opposition to the proposal to abolish
Community Health Councils.

Furthermore, the opposition is violently against the terms of
the Health Services Bill[4] that was introduced in Parliament in
December 1979. This is because the bill not only empowers the
Secretary of State to alter the structure of the NHS in accordance with the proposals of *Patients First* but also provides
for the abolition of the Health Services Board that was introduced by the Labour administration to phase out private practice from the NHS and to control the development of new
private hospitals. The bill also allows health authorities to
organize fund raising for their own hospitals and other health-
care projects — activities previously forbidden for any NHS
authority.

In a Parliamentary debate[5] on the bill, Mr. Patrick Jenkin,
the Secretary of State at the DHSS, defended the government's
decision to encourage private practice and said that in a free
society, patients who wish to seek private treatment should be
allowed to do so, and he quoted a national opinion poll that
showed that 60 per cent of working people would be interested
in having private medical insurance as part of their terms of
employment. Furthermore, the poll revealed that most health-
service-union members believed that they should cooperate in
providing private medicine, and only 11 per cent thought it the
job of their unions to oppose private medicine. Opposition
spokesmen denounced the bill on the grounds that it was a
private patients' charter, that the abolition of the Health Services Board and the phasing back of pay-beds in the NHS would
do more to harm industrial relations in the NHS than any
other measure, and that it would allow the private sector to
attract doctors and nurses away from the NHS. The proposal
to allow fund-raising appeals was criticized on the grounds

that the richer areas would gain the most and the poorer areas the least from such activities, and the public would give money for the most glamorous rather than the most urgent needs. Furthermore, successful fund-raising activities might tempt the Secretary of State to reduce the amount of exchequer funding to the districts concerned.

In replying for the government, the Under Secretary of State emphasized that any money raised by local voluntary fund raising would be an addition to the allocation made by the Secretary of State; the Under Secretary also reaffirmed the view of the government that the relation between the public and private sectors should be one of partnership and claimed that the policy of separate development in the two sectors embarked on by the previous administration had been misguided.

And of course the government has a majority large enough to ensure that its proposed legislation will be passed, although it is unfortunate that once again the case of the sick should be the subject of so much acrimonious debate. Nevertheless, for those most directly concerned with the care of patients it is encouraging that the government has made positive proposals that should ensure that the needs of patients, whether in the public or the private sector, do come first.

1. Report of the Royal Commission on the National Health Service. London: Her Majesty's Stationery Office, 1979.
2. Patients first — a consultative paper on the structure and management of the National Health Service in England and Wales. London: Her Majesty's Stationery Office, 1979.
3. Deitch R. The Government's proposals for the N.H.S. Lancet 1979; 2:1385-1386.
4. *Idem*. The Health Services Bill. Lancet 1979; 2:1310.
5. Minister contends that majority favour private medicine. The Times, December 20, 1979.

Reorganization, 1980 Style

The simplified administrative structure mentioned in *Patients First* involved the elimination of the 90 Area Health Authorities and the creation of a larger number of District Health Authorities to be directly accountable to the Regional Health Authorities. It was hoped that the elimination of one tier of administration would lead to definite financial savings. The appointed day for this second reorganization of the National Health Service was April 1, 1982, just eight years after the first reorganization. The degree of confusion has not been great, and the new District Health Authorities are trying hard to establish good relationships with the clinicians with whom they work.

Students of the British National Health Service (NHS) will recall that it was introduced on July 5, 1948, reorganized on April 1, 1974, and is about to be reorganized again. The reorganization that took place in 1974 has been widely criticized. One of the major objectives of this reorganization was to unify the administration of the hospitals, the general-practitioner service, and the public-health service — these three services having been separately administered since the introduction of the NHS. To some extent this unification was achieved in 1974, although general practitioners still hold contracts of service with family-practitioner committees rather than directly with the health authorities. However, it was the introduction of the 90 Area Health Authorities (AHA's), which formed a new administrative tier between Regional Health Authorities (RHA's) and the districts, that aroused the greatest criticism. These authorities simply enlarged the bureaucratic machine, increasing the number of administrators and often causing delays in decision making. When the present government took office it was committed to review the administrative arrangements of the NHS, and as previously reported,[1] a consultative document on this topic entitled *Patients First*[2] was published at the end of last year.

The Department of Health and Social Security received about 3500 comments from organizations and individuals about this document, and the Secretary of State, Mr. Patrick Jenkin, has now announced the government's proposals in a statement to Parliament.[3] As anticipated, the AHA's will be abolished and replaced by District Health Authorities (DHA's), which it is hoped will be much more responsive to local needs. The DHA's will serve populations of between 150,000 and 500,000, and it is suggested that they should be established for the smallest geographic areas within which an integrated service could be planned and developed. This would include the provision of primary care and other community health services and the services normally associated with a district general hospital, including provision for the elderly, the mentally ill, and the handicapped. RHA's will be responsible for making recommendations to the Secretary of State about the future pattern of these DHA's, and it is hoped that such recommendations will be received early next year so that most DHA's can be brought into formal existence by April 1, 1982, with all changes being completed by April 1, 1983.

Each DHA will be distinctly smaller than existing AHA's and will have only 16 members. The chairman will be appointed by the Secretary of State, and members will include one hospital consultant, one general practitioner, one nurse, and one member nominated by the university with a medical school in the region. Local authorities will appoint four members, and there will be representatives of trade unions and other interested parties. DHA's will have wide discretion in determining their management arrangements, but they will appoint district management teams, one of the more successful features of the 1974 reorganization, even though the principle of reaching decisions by consensus has not always proved too effective.

Mr. Jenkin also announced in his statement that the community health councils, which were set up in each district in 1974 to represent consumer interest, would be retained. It had been thought that they might be abolished, partly for economic purposes and partly because the presence of four members of the local authority on the new DHA's should make them less necessary. However, Mr. Jenkin admitted that he had found considerable support for the councils from those who commented on *Patients First*, and it had also been pointed out that their annual cost of £4 million was really very small. Mr. Jenkin indicated, however, that he intends to issue a consultative paper on their membership, role, and powers, and that after a few years of experience of the working of the new DHA's, he would review the longer-term case for retaining these separate consumer bodies.

Mr. Jenkin emphasized that the main purpose of the proposed changes is to provide a health service that is better and more efficiently managed, with decision making being brought down to the hospital and the community level. At the same time he hopes that it will be possible to reduce management costs by about 10 per cent, which would release about £30 million for patient care.

In the debate that followed his statement, opposition spokesmen took obvious delight in pointing out the irony of Mr. Jenkin's having to dismantle much of the administrative machinery created in 1974 by the last Conservative Secretary of State, Sir Keith Joseph. They were particularly concerned to know what plans Mr. Jenkin had in mind for coping with the staff redundancies that might occur. Nevertheless, there was general agreement that most of the present proposals are sound, and they have been generally welcomed by the lay press, although the *Daily Telegraph*[4] had some reservations. Thus, while one may welcome the exorcising of the bureaucratic, as opposed to the demonic, possession that has been consuming the NHS, one may regret that the present proposals are still just a reorganization rather than a rethinking or a redefinition. And while agreeing that the forthcoming reorganization appears benign when compared with that of 1974, the *Daily Telegraph* considers that it still shows an inadequate sense of accountability to the patient and suggests that the NHS will never really work until all tiers of administration and all administrators, doctors, and the rest are made answerable to the patient. This is certainly a fine sentiment that should be shared by all practicing physicians and others directly involved in patient care, but the *British Medical Journal* in a leading article[5] has emphasized that if patients are to benefit from this new reorganization there will have to be widespread changes of attitude. Thus, staff who regard the NHS primarily as a vehicle for their employment or who prefer confrontation to cooperation, patients whose expectations are unrealistically high, and pressure groups who see their special interest as the most urgent priority all undermine the NHS. If, however, such attitudes should change and the forthcoming reorganization should really succeed in devolving power, this could restore a sense of local pride, loyalty, and cooperation among staff, which would be to the benefit of all those who depend on the NHS.

---

1. Lister J. Patients first. N Engl J Med 1980; 302:508-509.
2. Patients first — a consultative paper on the structure and management of the

National Health Service in England and Wales. London: Her Majesty's Stationery Office, 1979.

3. Health Service to be streamlined by removing one tier of administration: £30 million saving. The Times, July 24, 1980.

4. Anonymous. Up Jenkin. Daily Telegraph, July 24, 1980.

5. *Idem.* New NHS structure needs new attitudes. Br Med J 1980; 281:342.

Inequalities in Health

NOVEMBER 27, 1980

Sir Douglas Black, president of the Royal College of Physicians of London, was at one time Chief Scientist at the Department of Health and Social Services. Because of one or both of these roles, he was asked to become chairman of a working group to review information about differences in health status between the social classes. The findings showed that in spite of improved health-care facilities in Britain there had been little improvement in the health of unskilled and semiskilled workers in the past two decades.

The working group was commissioned by a Labour government and reported to a Conservative government. It is perhaps not surprising that the reception given to this report by the Conservative Secretary of State at the Department of Health and Social Security was rather lukewarm, since he had estimated that an annual additional expenditure of £2 billion would be required to make the social changes thought to be necessary to rectify the deficiencies noted.

In 1977, Mr. David Ennals, then Secretary of State in the Department of Health and Social Security (DHSS), set up a working group to study the problems of inequalities in health. The chairman was Sir Douglas Black, president of the Royal College of Physicians of London, who was chief scientist at the DHSS at the time. The other members of the group were Prof. Norman Morris, professor of community health at the London School of Hygiene and Tropical Medicine, Dr. Cyril Smith, secretary of the Social Science Research Council, and Prof. Peter Townsend, professor of sociology at the University of Essex. Their report,[1] which runs to 417 pages, was published after its submission to Mr. Patrick Jenkin, the present Secretary of State at the DHSS.

The main objectives of the group were to review information about the differences in health status between the social classes, to consider possible causes of the differences and the implications for policy, and to suggest what further research should be initiated. Social classes were regarded as "segments of the population sharing broadly similar types and levels of resources with broadly similar styles of living." Such segments are conveniently recognized through a person's declaration of occupation. The present classification of social class ranges from Class I to Class V: the professions are ranked as Class I, followed by the managers in Class II, the skilled workers in Class III, the partly skilled workers in Class IV, and the unskilled workers in Class V.

In its report, the working group concentrated great attention on differences in mortality rates and on morbidity, and found that most recent data show marked differences in mortality rates between the occupational classes for both sexes and at all ages. Thus, at birth and in the first month of life twice as many babies of Class V parents die as do babies of Class I parents. Furthermore, in adult life a class gradient can be observed for most causes of death, with a particularly severe slope for diseases of the respiratory system. Data on chronic sickness tend to parallel those on mortality. It also appears that there has been little improvement and even some deterioration in the health of the unskilled and semiskilled workers in the past two decades.

Inequalities also exist in the use of health services, particularly preventive medicine, which is not fully used by the working classes. On the other hand, as would be expected from the data, those in Classes IV and V tend to make more use of their family physicians' services than do the middle-class people, although this level of use may not wholly reflect the true differences in the need for care, as shown by the mortality and morbidity figures.

Comparison of the findings in Britain with those in other industrial countries shows that British perinatal and infant mortality rates have been distinctly higher than those in the Netherlands and the Scandinavian countries. The adult mortality patterns, especially for men in the younger age groups, reasonably approximate those of other Western industrialized countries.

The working group does not believe that there is any single or simple explanation for the inequalities that they have revealed. But much of the evidence on social inequalities in health can be understood in terms of specific features of the socioeconomic environment, such as overcrowding, accidents at work, and cigarette smoking, all of which are strongly class-related in Britain.

Good antenatal care is probably important in preventing perinatal death; the group has concluded that early childhood is the period of life in which intervention could most probably weaken the continuing association between health and social class.

On the basis of these observations the group made a series of recommendations. Better collaboration between government departments is advised as a means to obtain reliable statistics about the health status of children in relation to the occupational class of their parents and to compile information about accidents to children, the incidence of which is closely related to social class. There is also a need for more effective methods of nutritional surveillance. But the group believes that the problem of social inequalities in health is so complex that the DHSS should enlist the expertise of the Medical Research Council and the Social Science Research Council in initiating an appropriate research program.

Meanwhile, the group makes certain recommendations on policy to give children a better start to life, i.e., encouraging good health by preventive and educational action and improving the quality of life for disabled people. To achieve these objectives, more resources should be shifted toward community care, particularly in the field of antenatal and postnatal care and the care of children. Better distribution of family doctors is also necessary, especially in areas of high prevalence of ill health and poor social conditions. If the number of family doctors is inadequate, local health authorities should deploy additional community nurses.

More active commitment by the DHSS and other government departments is required in the field of preventive medicine and health education; the working group emphasizes that much stronger measures should be introduced to reduce cigarette smoking. To reduce inequalities in health there is much to be done outside the health service. The abolition of poverty in childhood would require a redistribution of financial resources that would be far beyond anything achieved by past programs and would be very costly. It is suggested, however, that the level of benefits for children should be increased and that school meals should be provided without charge. The provision of better housing facilities should be given high priority by local authorities.

In all these matters the group emphasizes the need for better coordination between government departments in the administration of health-related policies. A health development council should be established, with an independent membership having a key advisory and planning role in a collaborative national policy to reduce inequalities in health.

In his foreword to the report, Mr. Jenkin congratulates Sir Douglas and his colleagues on the thoroughness with which they have studied the problem, and expresses disappointment that in the period since the inception of the National Health Service there has been little sign of any diminution of inequalities in health. He notes that the group believes that the causes of these inequalities are so complex that they could be corrected only by a major and wide-ranging program of capital expenditure. Indeed, he estimates that the cost might be as much as £2 billion a year — a figure that he regards as quite unrealistic in present or any foreseeable economic circumstances. He could not therefore endorse the group's recommendations, but he would make the report available for discussion, without any commitment by the government to its proposals.

It is understandable that Mr. Jenkin gave a cool reception to a report of this nature, which had been commissioned by his predecessor in office. Indeed, both the *British Medical Journal*[2] and the *Lancet*[3] could appreciate his reaction, but neither felt that such curt dismissal of the report was justified, since the topic is clearly of fundamental importance and worthy of serious debate and should be above party politics.

The *British Medical Journal* believes that the group has done a valuable service in emphasizing the importance of social welfare, housing, and educational services in maintaining high standards of health. On the other hand, it also points out that those trying to maintain standards in hospitals for the treatment of acute medical and surgical problems and also trying to reduce waiting lists for elective surgery are growing tired of being told that more money must be diverted from hospital care to community care.

The *Lancet* agrees that full implementation of the proposals in the report would increase public expenditure by an amount that would stagger even a Labour-Party Chancellor of the Exchequer. But not all the advice would be costly to implement. Similar advice has been given before, in such documents as *The Way Forward*,[4] which reviewed the need to assess priorities in the health and social services, and in the report of the Resource Allocation Working Party,[5] which identified the maldistribution of resources throughout the country and suggested methods for correcting it. Both of these reports were received by the last Labour government, and both gave the same message about the need for rethinking health policies, but that government did not truly grasp the reports' practical implications.

The *Lancet* believes that the publication of this new report raises issues about policy research, its commissioning, and its ultimate credibility, and suggests that there may be a need for independent research outside government, especially when policies are concerned. Such research does take place, in particular by bodies such as the Centre for Studies in Social Policy. The Centre is independent and nonpartisan, and its goal is to promote the analysis and discussion of the social dimension of public policy. In 1975 it published a book, *Inflation and Priorities*,[6] which reviewed the effects on the general welfare of society of such factors as housing, schools, unemployment, and the maintenance of law and order and the relation between the National Health Service and the personal Social Services.

For a practicing physician confronted with an individual patient, these matters must often seem remote, but for the politicians responsible for the welfare of the nation they are clearly of fundamental importance, and it is these politicians who must take the final responsibility for identifying priorities and acting appropriately. It must be hoped, therefore, that as the *Lancet* suggests, Mr. Jenkin will set up a critical and balanced group, with adequate resources, that would explore the possibility of implementing at least some of this new report's proposals for reducing the inequalities in health that have been revealed.

1. Department of Health and Social Security. Inequalities in health. London: Department of Health and Social Security, 1980.
2. Anonymous. Equalities and inequalities in health. Br Med J 1980; 281:762-763.
3. *Idem.* Inequalities in health. Lancet 1980; 2:513.

4. Priorities in the health and social services: the way forward. London: Department of Health and Social Security, 1977.
5. Resource Allocation Working Party. Sharing resources for health in England. London: Department of Health and Social Security, 1976.
6. Social policy and public expenditure: 1975: inflation and priorities. London: Centre for Studies in Social Policy, 1975.

The Last Post

My association with the *New England Journal of Medicine* has been one of the most rewarding experiences of my professional life. Looking over the contributions to the London Post over the years I realize that my perception of the importance of events may not always have been quite right, but through these contributions it is possible to identify the relative strength and weakness of the National Health Service, the political pitfalls into which politicians have fallen, and the fluctuating fortunes of the profession itself.

In this last Post I tried first to review the achievements and the failures of the first 32 years of the NHS and then to prognosticate for the next few decades. Time will be the judge.

I can still remember my first meeting with Dr. Garland, which took place in his office on the Fenway, in April 1952. I was on my first visit to the United States as a traveling fellow and, having been editor of a small medical journal that had literally died under my care, I had the temerity to pay a courtesy call upon the editor of the *New England Journal of Medicine*. I explained to Dr. Garland that I had greatly enjoyed receiving his journal in exchange for the *Clinical Journal*, which I had edited for H. K. Lewis, the London medical publishers, and I much regretted that since my journal had ceased publication, I could no longer expect to receive a regular complimentary copy of his. Dr. Garland expressed pleasure that I enjoyed his journal, regret that mine had ceased publication, and hope that his business manager might arrange for me to continue to receive the *Journal*.

He then mentioned that he had been thinking of having a London correspondent and asked if I knew of anybody who might serve as one, and if not, whether I might consider doing it myself. When I demurred he asked if there was anyone who would tell him whether I could do it, and whom I knew in the field of medical journalism. I mentioned Dr. Hugh Clegg, editor of the *British Medical Journal*, whom I assisted in a small way. This aroused great interest in Dr. Garland; he said that he would write to Dr. Clegg, that he would discuss matters with his editorial board, and that I might never hear from him again — but that on the other hand, I might. And off I went on my travels. A few days later, I wrote to Dr. Clegg, telling him that I had "taken his name in vain"; he wrote back that he had heard from Dr. Garland and had advised him to give me a trial. And so began my association with the *Journal* and a friendship with Dr. Garland that continued throughout the 15 remaining years of his editorship and then throughout his retirement.

It was Dr. Garland who named the column "By the London Post," and he was quite explicit about what he wanted — a column offering a commentary on medical affairs in Britain. He hoped that it would be peripatetic; it must not be dull and might even be lighthearted at times, but above all, the manuscript must arrive on schedule. I hope that I have satisfied at least some of these requirements, even though at times I may have been somewhat liberal in the interpretation of my brief. Quite often, Dr. Garland would not only acknowledge receipt of my manuscript but also would comment on the content in the clear, simple, and precise style that was the outstanding characteristic of his writing. In 1964, when I included a short piece entitled "Beatlemania," at the time the group known as the Beatles were first sweeping Britain with their rock-and-roll music, he sent me one of his most concise letters, which merely stated: "Thank you for the enclosure of January 16 — I never heard of a Beatle, am I a square? — as ever Joe." Later that year I wrote a serious note about birth control, which was acknowledged thus: — "Thank you for the Post for October which has just come to my desk. Certainly we need to get cracking on population control or we will all be standing on one leg like cranes."

But of course Dr. Garland was greatly interested in the British National Health Service (NHS), and inevitably much of my comment in the Post has been concerned with the evolution of the Service, its contribution to the health and welfare of the nation, and the effect that it has had on the medical profession. When Dr. Garland retired in 1967 and was succeeded by Dr. Franz Ingelfinger, I naturally thought that I should offer my resignation, but Ingelfinger asked me to continue. He always took great pleasure in reminding me about my first visit to his home in Cambridge, when Dr. Garland took me in his car and delivered me at his back door! When Dr. Ingelfinger retired in 1977, I had been writing the Post for 25 years, and I suggested to Dr. Arnold Relman that this must be a good time for me to retire, but he too persuaded me to continue a little longer, which has turned out to be for another three years. For this last contribution to the London Post, Dr. Relman suggested that as well as reflecting on the past, I should gaze into the crystal ball of the future. I agreed, although I did remind him that the art of retrospective diagnosis is much easier than the art of prognosis!

But first of all, let us look back. In 1952 the NHS was only four years old, and this great experiment in social welfare was being acclaimed by the politicians as the envy of the world. Before its introduction, British doctors had been in acrimonious negotiations with Aneurin Bevan, the Socialist Minister of Health, but eventually they came to terms with him, and after the Service was introduced on July 5, 1948, they set about collaborating with the government in running this new enterprise with considerable good will.

The general practitioners were able to retain their status as independent contractors, and although they accepted a basic practice allowance, the bulk of their income was derived from capitation fees. Hospital consultants and specialists were given the option of accepting full-time contracts, which excluded them from engaging in private practice, or part-time contracts, which allowed them to practice privately in the time that they did not devote to the NHS. Furthermore, Bevan agreed that about 1 per cent of the beds in the NHS hospitals would be made available for private patients.

Over the years the British people have seemed satisfied with the service that they have received from the NHS, which has given them access to health care without payment at the time of use — one of the basic principles of the Socialist interpretation of the Beveridge report.[1] On the other hand, the doctors, the nurses, and indeed almost every other group of health-care workers have been at some time or other in dispute with the NHS as an employer.

Reflecting on his experience as Minister of Health,[2] Enoch Powell claimed that money was the only topic that he had ever discussed with the doctors; they always wanted more, either for themselves or for their departments. He forecast that some form of rationing of health care would eventually be necessary, because the demands on the NHS would be infinite whereas the resources would be finite.

The extent of the escalation in the cost of the Service is reflected in the facts that when it was introduced, Bevan estimated that the annual cost would be £400 million, whereas this cost is now more than £10,000 million, and the Service is the largest employer of labor in the country.

During the 32 years since the NHS began, there has been an immense rise in the degree of professionalism in all the professions allied to medicine, while hospital aides, cleaners, cooks, and some nurses have joined trade unions that not only have used their powers to improve the terms and conditions of service of their members but also have resorted to industrial action to bring about political changes in the Service. A major result of this rise in professionalism and politicization of the NHS has been the loss of medical predominance in many aspects of delivery of health care.

Apart from conflicts over pay, doctors have been involved in other disputes with the government. The most serious of these concerned the question of private practice within the NHS, which the Labour party has sought to outlaw ever since the right to such practice was conceded in 1948. When Labour returned to power in 1974, it came with an election promise to separate private practice from the NHS. Barbara Castle, appointed Secretary of State for Health and Social Services, prepared legislation to achieve this end. Hospital consultants regarded this as a unilateral breach of the agreement reached with Bevan, and many were so incensed that they restricted their service to the minimum required by their contracts, and for a time the atmosphere in the hospitals was very sour. The Health Services Bill to effect the phasing out of private beds from hospitals and to monitor the development of private hospitals was eventually passed, but before all the private beds had been eliminated from the NHS, the Labour government was replaced by the present Tory government, which repealed the Health Services Act and adopted a totally contrary policy of encouraging private practice both inside and outside the NHS. This episode illustrates one of the major problems that has beset the NHS ever since its inception — namely, the repeated changes of direction to which it has been subjected because of differing philosophies of successive governments.

Now, let us look into the future. It is not easy to do so, but clearly the course that the practice of medicine will take in Britain in the coming decades will depend not only on the philosophy of the government of the day but also on the economic fortunes of the country and the attitudes of the public towards the technological advances that are continually taking place. If the Tory government remains in power, there will be increasing emphasis on self-reliance by those able to provide for themselves, and the private sector will continue to expand. It must be hoped, however, that such expansion will be on strictly ethical lines and that it will be the private hospitals with charitable status, rather than those that are run for profit, that will prosper. Furthermore, it is vital that the practice of medicine in the private sector should be of the highest standard and that this standard should be monitored at least as stringently as in the public sector. The private sector should not be open to the criticism that it is a parasite on the public sector, and it should train its own nursing staff and provide training opportunities for junior medical staff that are not inferior to those in NHS hospitals. At the same time, it must be hoped that Tory administrations will continue not only to support the NHS but also to improve the NHS facilities on which the majority of the population will continue to depend. Unless they do so, the NHS will deteriorate and will become a depressing organization within which to work and an unsatisfactory organization from which to seek treatment. But with good will and a fair distribution of resources, the public and private sectors should be complementary to each other in the service they offer and should exert mutually beneficial quality control on each other.

On the other hand, the return of another Socialist government would be followed by renewed efforts to eliminate private practice from the NHS, and if the resolutions of the recent Labour Party conference[3] were put into effect there would be an attempt to outlaw private practice in any form. The NHS would then have a complete monopoly in health-care delivery, but although the Labour party has declared that it would improve the NHS and eliminate all charges, the increase in public expenditure that would be necessary to achieve these ends might not be approved even by a Labor Chancellor of Exchequer.

But whatever government may be in power in the next few decades, there will be inescapable problems that will have to be faced. The most obvious of these difficulties is the increase in the number of elderly patients, particularly women. Furthermore, from a purely economic point of view it will be necessary to care for patients in the community rather than in institutions. The emphasis must therefore be on primary care by general practitioners, and it must be hoped that present efforts to improve the standard of general practice through the introduction of mandatory vocational training for general practitioners will achieve this goal. Economic circumstances will also dictate the need to set priorities; whatever the government in power, some kind of health-care rationing will be unavoidable. The benefit of high-technology medicine will have to be assessed; it may well be that the value of good clinical judgment and common-sense decisions will once again be recognized.

The medical profession will need to respond to whatever challenges arise. The experience of recent years has shown that doctors tend to react in the same way as other members of society. Junior hospital doctors, in their quest for a basic 40-hour week, and senior hospital consultants, in their defense of a right to private practice, were equally willing to resort to some form of industrial action to achieve their aims. I hope that such incidents will never recur; on this occasion the sense of frustration and the feelings of being wronged were so strong among both groups that many doctors believed themselves justified in taking such a course.

The increasing emphasis on the importance of primary care in the community by general practitioners has been accompanied by a tendency to denigrate the role of the hospital and the specialists. This development may have been quite unintentional, but there is a distinct danger that general practitioners are drifting apart from consultants and specialists — a very unhealthy situation for the profession and patients. There is an urgent need to encourage these two major components of the medical profession to work in harmony.

In the coming decades the question of medical manpower will need to be kept under close review; during this time the full impact of the increased number of women graduates will be felt. In most British medical schools women now compose nearly half the first-year students, and most of them are planning for active and nearly full-time participation in practice. They tend to select specialties most suited to combination with domestic commitments, and arrangements are being made for those able to work only on a part-time basis. The effect of this increased number of women graduates on the total number of doctors required will depend on the proportion of their working lives that they devote to medical practice. It will be some time before these events can be fully assessed.

These, then, are some of the problems of the next few years, and doubtless there will be many more. But now I must conclude, and want to say how greatly I have valued the privilege of sharing my thoughts with readers of the *Journal* over the past 28 years.

When I was honored to give the Garland Memorial Lecture last year, I chose the title "Sustaining the Common Language."[4] I did so because I thought it was a title of which Dr. Garland would have approved, and because I do believe that it is important that our common language be preserved in an intelligible form and that the style of practice in our two countries will continue to bear the mark of the clinical tradition on which both British and American medicine were founded. Recently it has been the British who have traveled to America for new ideas, but it says much for the stamina of the early members of the American medical profession that to further their training they were prepared to face the long and hazardous voyage to Europe. Indeed, at the time of the 150th anniversary of the founding of the *New England Journal of Medicine and Surgery and the Collateral Branches of Science* — the full title of the journal from which the present *Journal* claims its origin — Dr. Garland recalled[5] that the two Boston physicians John Collins Warren and James Jackson, the founders of the *Journal*, had spent time at Guy's Hospital in London and so gave the *Journal* a heritage of British standards and tradition. For my part, I believe that it is important that this special relationship between American and British physicians should be maintained, and I am sure that the best way of sustaining the Anglo-American dialogue in an intelligible form is for us to continue writing in each other's journals and for medical travelers to continue journeying across the Atlantic in both directions.

1. Beveridge W. Plan for social security, social insurance and allied services report. London: His Majesty's Stationery Office, 1942.
2. Powell JE. A new look at medicine and politics. London: Pitman, 1966.
3. Russell W. Abolish private practice, nationalise the drug industry. Br Med J 1980; 281:1017.
4. Lister J. Sustaining the common language (The Fourth Garland Memorial Lecture). Delivered at the Countway Library of Medicine, Boston, October, 1979.
5. Garland J. A voice in the wilderness — The "New England Journal of Medicine" since 1812. Br Med J 1962; 1:105-108.

The British Medical Scene Since 1980

The article reprinted below appeared just two years after "The Last Post," in which I reflected on the past and tried to look into the future. On balance, my prognostications were fulfilled, but the effects of some of the social, political, and professional developments were perhaps rather more dramatic than I had anticipated.

———————

Since the last London Post was written over two years ago,[1] the British medical scene has been unsettled on account of economic factors, government policy, and professional problems.

Whether the so-called monetarist policy of the Thatcher government is considered to be harsh or just realistic may depend on one's own political viewpoint, but it has undoubtedly had a profound effect on the National Health Service (NHS), the universities and their medical schools, and research activity. Even before the economic recession became serious, the NHS authorities were subjected to rigid budgetary limits, and because of the high rate of inflation many authorities have found that in real terms their budgets have been reduced. The proportion of the gross national product spent on health has remained no more than 6 per cent.

As anticipated, the present government has encouraged the expansion of the private sector in medicine, and during the first two years of its term of office there was a steep rise in the numbers of individual and business subscribers to private health-insurance plans. Thus, in 1980 the number of people covered by private insurance increased by 28 per cent, although in 1981 the increase was only 12 per cent, bringing the total number of people covered by private insurance to about 4 million.

During the same period there was also a rapid increase in the number of private hospitals; some were charitable, nonprofit institutions but others were profit making. The government has repeatedly called for a working partnership between the private and the public sectors, but this has been hard to establish and difficult to define. In fact, there has been some criticism that, far from complementing the work of the NHS, the private sector may be attracting skilled nursing and technical staff away from the NHS, from which most of them received their initial training.

There has also been concern about the escalating cost of hospital care in the private sector, particularly in the proprietary profit-making hospitals, many of which are owned by American companies. Indeed, the British United Provident Association, Britain's largest private health insurer, reported an underwriting loss of £1.9 million last year and attributed this to the high charges in the proprietary hospitals.

It is perhaps not surprising that the Labour party, at present in opposition, should have returned to the attack on private medicine. Labour threatens, if returned to power at the next general election, to eliminate all private practice from the NHS, to take over any institution in the private sector that might be useful to the NHS, and to disband the private health-insurance plans. Such radical measures might be difficult to bring about and would meet with the opposition of the large numbers of trade-union members who now carry private health insurance either individually or through their companies. On the other hand, such threats are disturbing and indicate the unsatisfactory effect that the swinging political pendulum can have on a service such as the NHS.

Apart from the issue of private practice, the government has encountered serious labor problems with the NHS; for much of 1982 the NHS was disrupted by various kinds of strikes. As part of its campaign to control inflation the government was determined to restrict expenditure in the public sector, and inevitably, pay raises had to be modest. Thus, those working in the NHS — incidentally, the largest employer in the United Kingdom — were offered raises ranging from 6 to 7.5 per cent, as compared with 12 per cent claimed by both nurses and ancillary workers. Doctors and dentists accepted an increase of 6 per cent, which was 3 per cent less than that recommended by the Doctors and Dentists Review Body. The Royal College of Nursing honored their undertaking that they would never take strike action, but for more than six months the two main unions representing hospital ancillary staff — the Confederation of Health Service Employees and the National Union of Public Employees — attempted to disrupt the health service by industrial action of various kinds. Some hospitals suffered only minor inconvenience, but for long periods other hospitals were only able to provide emergency service. The government remained adamant that the offers of 6 to 7.5 per cent could not be increased. Eventually a two-year settlement was agreed on; the unions accepted the government's offer for 1982 and a firm promise of a further 4½ per cent raise in 1983.

In order to avoid a repetition of such a long and bitter dispute the nurses are to have an independent review body to advise on their pay, in the same way as the doctors and dentists have their pay reviewed each year. Discussions are also to take place with the unions in order to find better ways of negotiating the pay of ancillary staff. Meanwhile, it is hoped that the NHS can get back to caring for patients. Waiting lists for elective surgery have increased greatly, and the morale of many hospital workers is low. A determined effort will be required to restore good working relationships.

It was unfortunate that the period of industrial strife should have occurred in the year when the NHS was being subjected to its second major reorganization. The first reorganization took place in 1974, when the previous tripartite administrative structure — hospitals, family medicine, and public health — was replaced by a single administrative system. However, at that time a new tier of management was introduced in which area health authorities were interposed between the large regional authorities and the district authorities where the health care was actually delivered. The role of the area authorities was never too clear, and their elimination was proposed almost from the time they were introduced. This eventually took place on April 1, 1982, when the 90 area health authorities were replaced by 200 district health authorities directly responsible to the 14 regional health authorities, which in turn were responsible to the Department of Health. One of the objectives of this reorganization was to reduce the cost of administering the health service. It is to be hoped that a slimmer administration will be more efficient and that the increased autonomy granted to district health authorities will lead to more sensitive administrative arrangements at the local level.

In the academic field there have also been serious financial problems during the past two years. Universities were instructed to charge foreign students full tuition; the penalty for failing to do so would be a reduction in their grants. This measure was greatly resented by many schools that had a long tradition of attracting students from overseas, often from underdeveloped countries. In 1982 there were severe cuts in the annual grants made to universities by the University Grants Committee. These cuts affected all faculties and, as reported in the *British Medical Journal*,[2] are likely to have serious effects on the practice of medicine. During the next two years as many as 300 academic posts with clinical responsibilities may be lost, and this will inevitably affect medical education, research, and the care of patients. The serious implications of this policy were stressed in the report of a working party set up by the Royal College of Physicians of London, under the chairmanship of Sir Douglas Black, the president, to consider the problems facing academic medicine.[3]

In its report the Royal College of Physicians Working Party pointed out that the effects of the present cuts would not be immediately apparent, but that if the strength of academic medicine in Britain were eroded there would be a decline in the quality of our doctors and the high reputation of British medicine abroad might be prejudiced. Furthermore, any threat to the well-being of academic medicine is a threat to the well-being of the NHS, because there is a direct contribution to health-service work by all clinical academic departments as well as by pathology departments. There are already visible signs of cuts in academic departments, with 17.5 per cent of clinical academic posts in London being frozen or totally lost.

Many medical schools will have difficulty in meeting their commitments to the increased number of medical students whom they had agreed to take before the cuts were imposed. The Royal College Working Party hoped that the government would recognize these problems and the importance of high educational standards. It was also stressed that overseas students should be encouraged to come to Britain for postgraduate training and not be discouraged by financial burdens. The Parliamentary Social Services Committee acknowledged that teaching, research, and service in medical schools and university hospitals will all be severely damaged by university cuts, and recommended that an extra £10 million should be made available over the next two years to protect the teaching of clinical medicine.[4] However, in its response to the report of the Social Services Committee the government, though recognizing the genuine concern about the effect of cuts, pointed out that there was no central resource to protect clinical medicine from the economies required in university education generally.[5] All these matters have provided a rather bleak background for the medical profession, which has been concerned about the career prospects of young doctors and aware that the dominant role of doctors in medical decisions is again being challenged.

For many years there has been great difficulty in establishing a satisfactory balance between the number of doctors in training and the number of career posts for those who are fully trained. The situation has not been too severe for those seeking a career in family practice, but for those aspiring to a specialist career, particularly in general medicine, obstetrics and gynecology, and general surgery, the competition is fierce and the opportunities for consultant appointments are few. On the other hand, there is inadequate recruitment in some specialties, including psychiatry, geriatrics, and pathology. Because of this problem the Social Services Committee, of which Mrs. Renee Short is chairperson, undertook a review of medical education with special reference to the number of doctors in the career structure in hospitals.

In its report the committee pointed out that consultants in the NHS work with teams of junior staff who, though in training, provide a great proportion of direct patient care.[6] Furthermore, because of the relatively small number of consultants — about 14,000 for the whole country — the age at which doctors in hospitals achieve full clinical independence is far too high. The committee has therefore recommended an increase in the number of consultants who would have more direct contact with individual patients. There would then be fewer junior doctors, whose training would be more effective and whose career prospects would be more realistic. The profession has now accepted these proposals in principle, and it must be hoped that financial constraints will not once again be the cause of delaying the implementation of these proposals. The committee also considered the hours of work of junior hospital doctors and thought it indefensible that many young doctors may be on call for more than 90 hours each week. This is a highly emotive subject, and the number of hours each week for which it is reasonable for a doctor in training to be on call must clearly vary from one specialty to another. Nevertheless, the committee advised a reduction in the number of hours in the junior doctors' contract to a maximum of 80 hours per week, with a possible further reduction at a later date. Many established physicians have argued that the practice of medicine cannot be confined to a specific number of hours each week, but the climate of opinion is such that young doctors are no longer prepared to accept open-ended responsibility for being on call, when their contemporaries in other professions are enjoying the benefits of a clearly defined work week. Furthermore, the leaders of the young doctors in training have claimed that the long hours of duty have placed an unreasonable strain on many residents, even to the extent of putting patients at risk on account of the doctors' fatigue. Hard evidence on this matter has been difficult to find, but it might be claimed that the lack of continuity of care that results from this type of shift-working medicine could be equally hazardous for patients.

It is also possible that the changing attitude of doctors regarding their responsibility to their patients may make physicians more vulnerable to pressure groups that would like to see the influence of the medical profession in many areas of decision making further reduced. The case for such a move was made with considerable eloquence by Ian Kennedy in the BBC Reith Memorial Lectures in 1980.[7] In this series of six half-hour lectures — named after Lord Reith, the first Director General of the British Broadcasting Corporation — Mr. Kennedy claims that the medical profession has assumed far too much responsibility for making decisions in matters concerning the welfare of patients, often without adequate consultation. As a lawyer and director of the Centre of Law, Medicine and Ethics at Kings College, London, and having held a number of similar appointments in the United

States, he clearly believes that he can speak with authority on the subject.

In the first lecture, entitled "The Rhetoric of Medicine," he suggests that the practice of medicine has changed, that there is a feeling abroad that all may not be well, and that this feeling is due to a sense that medicine is in the hands of experts and sets its own course. He believes that many troubling issues, such as heart transplantation, the definition of death, the treatment of the dying, and the treatment of the mentally ill, are inadequately discussed because the issues appear to be medical and technical and not really for the lay public. He says that to look behind the mask of modern medicine, it is necessary to unravel its rhetoric; by doing so consumers could become the masters of medicine, not its servants, so that they could have the power and set the policies in the politics of medicine.

In the next lecture, entitled "The New Magicians," he criticizes the present training of doctors, with what he considers its undue emphasis on the scientific aspects of medicine. He characterizes the modern doctor as an engineer/mechanic who is expected to dispense cures. Doctors are encouraged to adopt the mentality of problem solvers, with too much emphasis on crisis intervention and not enough on preventive medicine and positive attitudes toward the maintenance of good health.

In the field of decision making Mr. Kennedy believes that the doctor's present dominant role requires very close scrutiny. He believes that doctors are making ethical decisions in a haphazard, idiosyncratic way. He states that the fate of too many handicapped babies has been determined by medical decisions and that there should be more consultation in cases in which treatment to prolong life may be withheld on account of the age or frailty of the patient. He also believes that too often it is the doctor who decides how much a patient should be told about his or her condition. In the field of reproduction and birth there are many situations, such as abortion, artificial insemination, and genetic counseling, in which doctors may not always realize the ethical implications of the decisions they are making.

Mr. Kennedy devoted his final lecture to the subject of consumerism. He believes that consumer interests should take a more positive attitude toward the promotion of health by all manner of pressure groups. The consumer should also become more involved in determining the direction taken in the field of medical research. He also believes that consumerism has a role in the day-to-day practice of medicine. In medicine the consumer is the patient who is interested in self-determination and the power to participate responsibly in decisions made about his life. The challenge to that power comes from the doctor, who in exercising a professional role, threatens to treat the patient as an infant, to undermine his power of self-determination, and to act in a paternalistic manner. Mr. Kennedy suggests that consumerism should establish standards that doctors should meet in their practice, measure their performance against these standards, and impose sanctions against those who fail to meet them. He does not believe that self-regulation by the profession would be effective, but thinks that there is a need for an entirely new tribunal or review body. Consumers would need to be prominently represented by any such body, which would exercise a new system of supervision of the medical profession, with power to impose sanctions and suspend the incompetent or even remove from practice those found to merit removal whether on grounds of incompetence or ethical impropriety.

Mr. Kennedy freely admits that he was being provocative in his comments in the hope that they would stimulate debate. They might have been more effective if they had been less abrasive, for there is substance in some of his strictures. Medicine has become highly scientific, and it is clearly important that students should learn to care, as well as diagnose and treat, if the promoters of the various forms of alternative medicine are not to usurp the traditional role of the physician.

It is also clear that modern medical science has created many new ethical problems and that patients and their relatives must be informed and consulted so that they can participate in any ethical decisions. Such participation presents no threat to the doctor who recognizes that his role should be to give the right advice to the best of his ability. If he does so in all circumstances, he should have no fear from any tribunal or review committee. But of course the imposition of such a body would be a challenge to the claim of doctors that they belong to a profession rather than a trade, because one of the prime characteristics of a profession is that it is self-regulatory.

To a considerable extent this regulation is exercised by the General Medical Council, which was set up as the result of the Medical Act of 1858. This body may have its imperfections, but the Medical Act of 1978 has given it new responsibilities, particularly in the fields of postgraduate and continuing education. However, it must be recognized that Mr. Kennedy is questioning what he sees as an unreasonable degree of medical dominance in many aspects of medicine. This is now a familiar challenge that should be heeded. The profession can best meet it by ensuring that its own self-regulatory functions are effective.

1. Lister J. The last post. N Engl J Med 1980; 303:1528-1531.
2. Good and bad news for medical schools. Br Med J 1982; 284:1658.
3. Royal College of Physicians Working Party. Report of the Working Party on problems facing academic medicine. Presented to the College, July 1982.
4. Social Services Committee. UGC cuts and medical services. London: Her Majesty's Stationery Office, 1982.
5. Government response to the first report from the Social Services Committee, 1981-82 session. London: Her Majesty's Stationery Office, 1982.
6. Social Services Committee. Medical education with special reference to the number of doctors and the career structure in hospitals. 1980-81 session. 4th report. Vol. 1. London: Her Majesty's Stationery Office, 1981.
7. Kennedy I. The unmasking of medicine. London: Allen & Unwin, 1981.

Private Medical Practice and the National Health Service

OCTOBER 18, 1984

The place of private practice has been a matter of controversy ever since the National Health Service was established in 1948. Mr. Aneurin Bevan granted consultants the right to private practice both within and outside NHS hospitals. In 1974 Mrs. Barbara Castle sought unsuccessfully to eliminate private practice from the NHS. Since 1979 the Thatcher government has encouraged the continuation of a private–public "mix." Nevertheless, the controversy continues. The more important issues involved are reviewed in this article, which was based on the Edward L. Young Memorial Lecture presented at the Faulkner Hospital, Boston, May 15, 1984.

The essence of private medical practice lies in the nature of the relationship between patients and their physicians. In its most simple form this relationship is characterized by patients' making their own choice of doctors, establishing a direct contract with them, and being responsible for meeting their professional fees and other medical or surgical expenses.

The intervention of a third party, in the form either of some type of national health service or of an insurance carrier, has modified the relationship so that the distinction between public and private patients is less clear than before.

However, as Iglehart[1,2] has pointed out in his perceptive articles on the British National Health Service (NHS) under the Conservatives, the present British government is actively encouraging the growth of private medicine, and certain developments are taking place that could create problems similar to some of those causing concern in the United States.

It may therefore be helpful to consider the way in which the present structure of the medical profession in Britain has evolved and to see how the small private medical sector relates to the NHS, which was introduced in 1948 and is now the monopolistic employer of medical and nursing labor and the provider of medical care for more than 90 per cent of British citizens.

One of the most distinctive features of the present structure of the medical profession in Britain is the differentiation between general practitioners, who are responsible for primary care, and hospital consultants offering specialist services. Different concepts have been associated with the term "general practitioner" at different periods and in different countries, but as Brotherston[3] has explained, general practice emerged as a clear concept in Britain in the early 19th century. The term was used to describe the work of a medical practitioner who did everything of which he and medical knowledge were capable, whether medical, surgical, obstetric, or pharmaceutical. He usually had bed privileges at his local hospital. Specialization within medicine and surgery began in the late 19th century, but it was not until later that the proliferation of specialties and subspecialties began to infringe seriously on general practice. Eventually, the number of general practitioners with hospital-bed privileges began to decline, and most general practitioners began to concentrate on the role of family physician. In order to ensure that their incomes were protected, the system of referral of patients from general practitioners to specialists became established, and it was considered unethical for a specialist to see a patient without a letter of referral from his or her general practitioner.

The National Insurance Act was introduced by Lloyd George in 1911, but apart from workers with low incomes who were covered by the provisions of the act, all other patients had direct contracts with their family doctors. Bad debts were common, however, and many poor patients never received a bill.

In hospitals, most of which were voluntarily supported, patients contributed to the cost of their care according to their ability to pay. The visiting staff of specialists held honorary appointments, and for their living they relied on their private practices, which in turn depended on the referrals they received from general practitioners who were satisfied with the service the specialists offered to their public patients.

This was the relationship between general practitioners and specialists — or consultants, as they came to be known — right up to the time that the NHS was introduced in 1948.

It will be recalled that one of the main proposals of the 1942 Beveridge report[4] on social security was that a comprehensive health service should be established. This would ensure that "for every citizen there would be available whatever medical treatment he requires in whatever form he requires it, domiciliary or institutional, general, specialist or consultant and will ensure the provision of dental, ophthalmic and surgical appliances, nursing and midwifery and rehabilitation after accidents."

Beveridge did not exclude some forms of copayment by patients for services rendered, but when the NHS was introduced by the postwar Labour government, with Aneurin Bevan as minister of health, the plan's most fundamental principles were that no charges of any kind were to be levied on patients at the time they used the service and that all hospitals were to be taken into public ownership.

The medical profession was largely in sympathy with the principles of the Beveridge report. Furthermore, many doctors — particularly general practitioners — had small and rather uncertain incomes and welcomed the prospect of financial security and freedom from the need to pursue bad debts. Indeed, in the preface to *The Doctor's Dilemma*,[5] Bernard Shaw wrote, "To make matters worse doctors are hideously poor — Better be a railway porter than an ordinary English general practitioner."

But some of Bevan's proposals were unacceptable. The doctors were wholly opposed to a full-time salaried service and feared that the intervention of the state might compromise their clinical freedom and their relationships with their patients and might jeopardize their livelihood. They therefore resisted, negotiated, and finally compromised. As a result, general practitioners were allowed to retain their self-employed status as independent contractors with incomes derived mainly from capitation fees based on the number of patients registered on their practice lists.

Visiting hospital staff — the consultants and specialists — were offered the alternatives of full-time contracts, which denied them the right of private practice, or part-time contracts, which allowed them to engage in private practice during the part of the week that they did not contract to spend on NHS hospital work. It was also agreed that approximately 1 per cent of hospital beds would be available for private patients, who would pay the full cost of their accommodation and would pay the consultants for their services.

It was on this basis that the medical profession agreed to cooperate in running the NHS when it was introduced in 1948. In the early years it worked well and had the good will of the doctors, nurses, and all others working in it. However, it has suffered from repeated changes of policy due to the swinging political pendulum, with Labour administrations pursuing socialist policies and Conservative administrations trying to redress the balance.

One of the areas in which the positions of the two parties differ the most relates to private practice. The Labour party has always resented the concession made by Bevan to consultants with respect to private practice, and this has been the cause of much conflict. General practitioners soon found that there was little advantage to themselves in having private patients. They found that they could earn an adequate income from the NHS and claimed that they offered all patients, whether private or not, the same service.

On these grounds many general practitioners actively discouraged private patients, and a further disincentive to private general practice was the fact that private patients cannot receive prescription drugs through the NHS but must pay the full cost of all drugs prescribed. In the larger cities — particularly in London — there have always been a few general practitioners who have either practiced entirely privately outside the NHS or had small NHS lists and devoted most of their time to private practice.

The private sector therefore chiefly concerns consultants and specialist practice. Before the introduction of the NHS it was the tradition not only for the wealthy but also for middle-class, managerial, and professional people to see consultants privately and to have private or semiprivate hospital accommodations when necessary. With the introduction of the NHS many such people decided that they would, or perhaps felt that they should, avail themselves of the service. There was even a suggestion that their presence in the public sector might help to monitor its standards, since it was suggested that they might be more vocal in complaining about deficiencies than less discerning or less self-assured patients. However, the crowded outpatient clinics, the long waiting times for elective surgery, and the lack of privacy in many hospital wards were some of the factors that encouraged the development of a private sector partly within, and partly alongside, the NHS.

In theory, the choice of physician or surgeon has been retained in the NHS, since general practitioners are able to refer their patients to the consultant of their choice. However, the choice may ultimately be dictated by the fact that a certain clinic can offer the first appointment, and the patient may sometimes see not the named consultant but one of his registrars (residents) in training. Similarly, patients admitted as emergency cases come under the care of the admitting physician or surgeon, and in the NHS the majority of emergency operations are performed by registrars, although it is the responsibility of the consultants to satisfy themselves about the registrars' competence; the consultants themselves remain ultimately responsible for all patients admitted under their care.

It is relevant to mention at this point that the number of consultants in the NHS is relatively small — not more than 14,000 in all specialties — so that the hospital service is led by consultants but not fully staffed by them. Indeed, one of the major concerns in Britain today is the unsatisfactory career structure for aspirants to the hospital specialties, the ratio of those in training grades to those in career grades being far too high.

It has been suggested that established consultants have been reluctant to agree to an increase in the numbers of consultants because this would increase the competition for private patients. There may have been some truth to this suggestion in the past, but it is probably not an important factor now. In any case, one of the arguments put forward by those who defend the case for private medicine has been that it has helped to maintain the standards of the NHS, and some degree of competition should, in theory at least, be good for the maintenance of standards. In fact, in the earlier years of the NHS the only way to establish a sound base for a private consultant practice was to offer a good service for general practitioners and their hospital patients. Only when general practitioners were satisfied with the way their NHS patients were treated would they begin referring patients privately. Furthermore, when most private patients were admitted to private rooms in NHS hospitals, consultants frequently visited their hospitals outside their normal hours of duty and always sought out their resident staff to inquire about any problems on the public wards.

As has already been mentioned, the consultants only agreed to enter the NHS when Aneurin Bevan granted them the option of part-time contracts that would allow them to continue in private practice and agreed that a small number of private beds would be available in NHS hospitals. Private patients had to meet the full cost of their accommodations and nursing care, but from the beginning there were problems about the provision of any extra amenities for them. Indeed, there was a suspicion in some hospitals that care was taken to ensure that no special amenities were provided. Nevertheless, the agreement was honored for many years.

While Mr. Kenneth Robinson was minister of health, from 1964 to 1968, consultants began to be accused of various kinds of abuses related to their private practices. "Queue jumping" by private patients was a major complaint; it was claimed that patients who consulted specialists in their private offices were given preferential places on the waiting list for admission to NHS hospitals. Mr. Robinson conducted an inquiry but found little factual evidence to support the accusation. He also instituted a review of the occupancy rate for the private beds and, finding it low, he reduced their number to match the apparent demand. It may be that even then consultants were beginning to use the new private hospitals in preference to private beds in NHS hospitals because they were aware of the growing antagonism of some members of the NHS staff — particularly ancillary workers — to private practice in NHS hospitals.

However, it was while Mrs. Barbara Castle was secretary of state at the Department of Health and Social Security, during the years 1974 to 1976, that the major confrontation with consultants on this issue took place. Trade-union policy toward private practice hardened, and the Labour government agreed that private practice should be phased out of the NHS and controlled from outside, believing that it would not be possible to outlaw it altogether.

Mrs. Castle recognized that the implementation of such radical measures would precipitate a crisis, and she tried to negotiate with the consultants. However, the NHS trade unions — the National Union of Public Employees and the Confederation of Health Service Employees — were impatient and took matters into their own hands. In some hospitals they withdrew services from private patients, and in others they demanded the right to examine waiting lists in search of evidence of queue jumping by private patients.

Eventually, under pressure from these trade unions, Mrs. Castle announced plans for phasing private practice out of the NHS. The consultants considered this to be a breach of their contract, and the British Medical Association recommended that they should embark on industrial action and only operate an emergency service.

Not surprisingly, this tarnished the image of the consultants in the minds of the public, but it did stimulate further negotiations, which led to a considerable modification of Mrs. Castle's proposals. Nevertheless, she introduced legislation that provided for the establishment of a Health Services Board, which was to supervise the phasing out of private beds from the NHS; it also provided for control of the development of new private hospitals with more than 75 beds. Many believe that this plan to phase out private beds was a serious mistake because it was one of the factors that stimulated the growth of the private sector outside the NHS and the building of many small private hospitals.

In 1979 a Conservative government was returned to power, Mrs. Thatcher became prime minister, and the attitude to private practice was immediately changed. Instead of being discouraged, it was to be encouraged; soon the Health Services Board was disbanded, and the program to phase private beds out of NHS hospitals was halted.

The number of subscribers to the three main private health insurers — British United Provident Association (BUPA), Private Patients Plan (PPP), and Western Provident Association (WPA) — increased sharply. Furthermore, the subscribers were by no means all middle or upper class. Many companies arranged for group plans and paid the premiums for their employees, so that many working-class patients became insured for private treatment. In some parts of the country the police and fire departments took out private insurance for their members, and one large union negotiated the inclusion of private health insurance as part of a wage agreement. Although this is, of course, normal practice in the United States, it is evidence of a total change of attitude for a British trade union, and it provoked criticism from some other unions, particularly the health-service unions. This increase in the number of subscribers to private health-insurance plans was a further stimulus for an increase in the number of beds in the private sector outside the NHS.

During the past few years many small private hospitals have been built. Few have more than 100 beds, few can provide full facilities for intensive care, and although there is an increasing tendency to employ one or two resident medical-staff members, there is no way that these hospitals can provide satisfactory residency training programs. Nevertheless, many provide adequate facilities for routine surgical procedures, and they are popular with patients who carry sufficient private insurance to meet the cost. Most have achieved a reasonable rate of bed occupancy. Some of these hospitals are not for profit and are managed by charitable trusts. More recently, a number of investor-owned hospitals have been opened, some of them operated by American corporations. It is with respect to profit-making investor-owned hospitals that there has been some concern about this development. Although these hospitals are small, they are all well equipped and able to provide adequate facilities for uncomplicated surgical procedures and for routine medical diagnostic workups. Every attention is paid to the standard of amenities provided for the patients. These hospitals also appear to be efficiently run, but they are expected by their parent corporations to show a profit. Although the daily bed charge may be kept within the range agreed to by the British United Provident Association or the Private Patients Plan, the markup on "extras" (referred to as "ancillary services" in the United States) tends to result in an inflated bill. Indeed, two years ago the British United Provident Association reported an operating loss, with claims exceeding premiums. This was partly attributed to the large number of claims by new subscribers, particularly among those in group plans that included full family coverage, but another important factor was the number of heavy claims resulting from admissions to investor-owned hospitals. Discussions took place between the management of these hospitals and the insurance carriers, but a steep rise in premiums was unavoidable, and this led to a falloff in the number of new subscribers and the cancellation of some existing subscriptions. This experience lends support to the view that the private sector in British medicine will probably never increase to cover more than about 10 per cent of the population unless a radical restructuring of the method of funding the NHS is introduced. Mrs. Thatcher was thought to have favored the substitution of the present, centrally funded NHS with some form of compulsory health insurance such as those in many other countries but was persuaded that it would be politically unwise to make the changes.

At present, therefore, the philosophy is that the public–private "mix" should continue. In theory, the government encourages the growth of the private sector, but so far it has not made private health-insurance premiums tax-deductible for individual subscribers, although lower-paid workers who receive private health insurance as part of wage agreements are not taxed on the premiums.

The existence side by side of not-for-profit charitable hospitals and profit-making investor-owned hospitals in the small British private sector holds an important lesson both for Britain and for the United States. The not-for-profit charitable hospitals genuinely seek to provide at minimal cost what the patients require. However, they are subject to the constraint that though they are not operating for a profit they cannot operate at a loss either; thus, there has to be some margin between actual costs and the fees charged in order to provide for all contingencies and to ensure solvency.

On the other hand the profit-making investor-owned hospitals seek to generate work in order to generate profit. When challenged about the profit-making motive in the health-care field, their answer is that doctors make a profit from treating patients, and therefore why should not investor-owned hospitals do the same for their investors?

Such a positive attitude toward profit making can of course only lead to further escalation of the cost of health care when most responsible observers are concerned about cost containment. Relman[6,7] has written eloquently about this problem, particularly in relation to investor-owned hospitals. He has also raised the issue of the financial involvement of physicians in health-care businesses and suggested that the voice of the medical profession would carry more moral authority if it adopted the principle that practicing physicians should derive no financial benefit from the health-care market except from their own professional services.

In Britain the medical profession is regulated by the General Medical Council, which states[8]: "If a doctor or his or her spouse owns or holds shares in an organisation which advertises diagnostic or clinical services to the public: i) the doctor should not also work for it in a clinical capacity; ii) the doctor should not use or permit the use of his professional qualifications in communications addressed by the organisation to the public as an advertisement for the organisation or be personally involved in advertising its services, for example by public speaking, broadcasting, writing articles or signing circulars."

Fellows of the Royal College of Physicians of London are constrained by the bylaws[9] of the College, which state: "[I]t is undesirable that any Fellow or Member of the College should have any financial interest (whether direct or indirect) in any Company or Institution having for its object the treatment of disease for profit, other than the receipt by him from such Company or Institution of (1) a fixed salary, or (2) fees for such services as he may render to such Company or Institution in his capacity as medical adviser."

In spite of these constraints there has been some concern in Britain about the involvement of physicians in various aspects of the health-care business. In particular, there are doctors who have financial interests in hospitals and clinics where they treat patients. The chairman of the Independent Hospitals Group has said[10]: "We are seeing a new breed of consultant [specialist] who would like to see a financial return for his contribution to the hospital and who is interested in getting a true commercial dividend from the investment involved."

The Charity Commissioners[11] have now ruled that consultants who are directors or trustees of private hospitals with charitable trusts must not treat patients in them privately. The General Medical Council and the British Medical Association have also been asked to consider ruling that consultants should not be allowed to invest in investor-owned hospitals and then treat patients in them. The General Medical Council[12] has responded by ruling that when a doctor refers a patient to a hospital in which he has an interest, whether for treatment by himself or by another, he must do so only in a way that will best serve the medical interests of the patient and he must disclose that he has such an interest before making the referral.

In his article on changing philosophies in medical care and the rise of the investor-owned hospitals, Cunningham[13] refers to the code of ethics formulated by Sir Thomas Percival in

1803, in which it was stated, "The prime object of the medical profession is to render service to humanity; reward or financial gain is a subordinate consideration." He also quotes Dr. Pellegrino,[14] former president of the Catholic University of America, who said, "The hospital or social agency that designates itself as non-profit making and speaks of 'serving' the community makes an explicit promise. That promise, to be competent and to serve the best interests of the patient, is the source of the moral obligation of all health professions. The hospital, too, promises the same things, but as a corporate entity."

At present it is unrealistic to suggest that physicians should regard their financial gains as unimportant considerations. They have families to support and children to educate and do not wish to be dependent on the charity of society. The real issue is whether physicians should be paid by the state or whether they should retain their traditional professional relationship with their patients, and whether in a country where there is a national health service there is any ethical objection to the coexistence of a private sector. Klein[15] has tried to answer these questions. He points out that the medical profession would claim that the right to private practice must be preserved as an expression of freedom and autonomy, which is of value not only to doctors but also to their patients.

The most familiar argument against private medical practice is that it allows a minority to buy special privileges. There is little evidence to support any claim that private patients in Britain receive better care, but they do buy the time of their consultants, and the waiting times for private appointments are usually shorter than in the NHS.

There have been complaints that the private sector diverts personnel away from the NHS. This applies particularly to nurses, virtually all of whom receive their training in the NHS. However, Klein believes that while the private sector remains small it is no real threat to the NHS, but were it to expand, the freedom of the medical profession within it might contract.

There are those who claim that the standards of the NHS should be so high that no one could see any benefit in being a private patient, so that private practice would eventually disappear spontaneously. Unfortunately, this utopian dream is in the far distant future. Private practice will therefore continue, but it is important that physicians should practice within accepted ethical guidelines.

1. Iglehart JK. The British National Health Service under the Conservatives. N Engl J Med 1983; 309:1264-1268.
2. *Idem.* The British National Health Service under the Conservatives — part II. N Engl J Med 1984; 310:63-67.
3. Brotherston J. Evolution of medical practice. London: Oxford University Press, 1971:85.
4. Beveridge W. Plan for social security, social insurance and allied services report. London: His Majesty's Stationery Office, 1942.
5. Shaw GB. The doctor's dilemma. London: Constable, 1906.
6. Relman AS. The new medical-industrial complex. N Engl J Med 1980; 303:963-970.
7. *Idem.* The future of medical practice. Health Affairs 1983; 2(2):5-19.
8. Professional conduct and discipline: fitness to practise. London: General Medical Council, 1983:22.
9. The By-Laws of the Royal College of Physicians of London. London: Royal College of Physicians, June 1982:67.
10. Doctors' financial interests challenged. The Times, January 16, 1984.
11. Ruling bans treatment by trustee consultants. The Times, May 8, 1984.
12. Doctors to declare hospital investment. The Times, June 2, 1984.
13. Cunningham RM Jr. Changing philosophies in medical care and the rise of the investor-owned hospital. N Engl J Med 1982; 307:817-819.
14. Pellegrino E. Foreword. In: Williams K, Donnelly P, eds. Medical care quality and the public trust. Chicago: Pluribus Press, 1982.
15. Klein R. Is there a case for private practice? Br Med J 1975; 4:591-592.

INDEX